Vet for hire

by
Russell Lyon

VET FOR HIRE

Published by The Good Life Press Ltd. 2011

ISBN 978 1907866067

A catalogue record for this book is available from

the British Library.

Published by

The Good Life Press Ltd.

The Old Pigsties

Clifton Fields

Lytham Road

Preston

PR4 0XG

www.goodlifepress.co.uk

www.homefarmer.co.uk

Chapters

Chapter 1
Introduction 513
Chapter 2
A Backward Glance 1422
Chapter 3
Mistakes! I've made a few 2334
Chapter 4
Fat Baby & the Sex Change 3546
Chapter 5
Fenland Characters 4764
Chapter 6
Pampered Pets 6577
Chapter 7
Eat to Live 7890
Chapter 8
Foregin Bodies 91 99
Chapter 9
How Cruel can you Be? 100 111
Chapter 10
Midlnight Medicine 112 117
Chapter 11
Bread and Butter 118 128
Chatper 12
Home and Away 129 142
Chatper 13
Vet for Hire....Still 143 150

For my grandchildren:

Jack, Danny, Rosie, Holly, Heather and Becky (Boo Boo!)"

Chapter One
Introduction

I have to admit that I have never enjoyed the business aspects of owning a practice. I was always much happier to be out on a call or in the operating theatre, and if I knew we were due for a VAT inspection you would not see me for dust, leaving these sorts of details to my accountant.

I have spent most of my veterinary career as a partner, then as a sole owner of a very mixed veterinary practice. My time as an assistant (salaried) veterinary surgeon was short. Within eighteen months of graduating I was offered an equal partnership in what became Noble, Jackson and Lyon, Veterinary Surgeons.

Alec Noble retired and Peter Jackson left for health reasons and pastures new in Edinburgh and was replaced by Elaine Stuttard and we carried on the practice for several years until we decided to go our separate ways. She founded a new and successful small animal veterinary clinic and I carried on with my mixed practice treating horses, farm animals and pets.

Fortunately, with my aversion for paperwork, I had a very good practice manager (Janet Marsh) and an excellent secretary (Kathy Ayres) who shouldered most of the day to day concerns that come with any business, but during private moments I would often envisage a life without the hassles of business worries and long to be just a vet again, concerned only with the clinical care of my patients.

One of the most onerous aspects of being in practice is the necessity of providing 24 hour emergency cover 365 days

Vet for Hire

a year. As a young vet it was an aspect of the job which I took in my stride. After all it was an aspect of veterinary life I had signed up to when I decided my career was going to be in general practice. I became involved in daily and weekly rotas and tried to make sure that the workload was shared out equally with the other vets in the practice.

As you can imagine it was not a job I enjoyed and when one of my younger colleagues (Catherine Mair) looked over my shoulder and said, "I don't know what you are complaining about. It really can't be that difficult," she was rewarded for her temerity. I passed the rota duty over to her with a sigh of relief. She actually admitted a few weeks later that this rota business wasn't as easy as she had first thought – I did not offer to take back my former duties.

The Christmas rota was always particularly fraught with difficulty.

"It's going to be different this year," said Janet, my head nurse and practice manager, looking purposefully in my direction. We were having one of those informal practice meetings over coffee which I always preferred to the more formal type with an agenda. I lifted a quizzical eye by way of acknowledgement, sat back with mug in hand and waited for the rest which was sure to follow. "This Christmas," she said, "We must get the rota organised."

"But it's only October," I said somewhat feebly. "I usually don't think about the rota until the first week of December."

"That's why it's going to be different this year," came the reply.

"Why can't you vets be organised like the nurses? Our rota is fixed four years in advance. Why can't you vets be like that?"

Introduction

I could have told her but in the interests of practice harmony I desisted. It had something to do with never being sure when an Aussie colleague would want to go 'walkabout' or a Kiwi might want to go skiing at the last minute or... but I did not go on. I knew when I was beaten. Janet had that look in her eye.

Before I knew it the vets' meeting was organised and almost simultaneously taking place. With Janet in charge I was soon jolted out of any feelings of complacency I had had with Christmas still so far away.

"Did I know," she said "Who was going to be the fourth vet at Christmas time this year?"

I didn't for the reasons already given about Aussies and Kiwis. But just for once I was ready with my answer.

"It will be," I announced, somewhat grandly in the style of a rugby team manager when the coach hasn't quite decided who will be in the team, "A. N. Other"

The reply was swift and brutally to the point.

"In that case it looks like you and A.N.Other are on again over Christmas."

It was another reason I was glad to get rid of the rota organiser's job to Catherine.

***

Most young vets now joining the profession have a much better regard for the work based on life balance, and most would much rather not be in a job which requires the long hours to which I and my peers had been accustomed. Many practices now try to share calls to reduce the time each vet has to be on duty. If the practice is in a large conurbation with a

Vet for Hire

high pet population they can use a 24 hour centre where there are vets and nurses on a shift system working throughout the night. Usually around 6.30pm the practice phone is switched over to the emergency centre or paging service and the vets and nurses can go home with a clear conscience, knowing that out-of-hours problems will be dealt with properly, and they can take over again at 8.30am next morning.

This is fine except in country areas where I have always worked. There is often not enough work to support a 24 hour centre. Farm and equine practices in particular struggle to provide (but still always do) a comprehensive care as sick animals take no notice whether it is the weekend or four o'clock in the morning. For vets working in those circumstances it is still very much a way of life and not a nine to five job. Where I work now six small animal clinics share on call duties and the night and weekend work is much reduced. A vet will only have to work a weekend perhaps every 3 months and one night on duty every 8-10 days. This is much better for most vets but the down side is that when you are working the unsocial hours you know you are going to be really busy. You can be up all night doing an emergency operation but will still be required to work as normal next day.

These improved conditions still seem light years away from those of modern GPs who have managed to divest themselves entirely of out-of-hours service, leaving a situation where it is reported that just two doctors can be responsible overnight for hundreds of thousands of patients.

It is not a situation that pet owners, the farming community or the equine world would tolerate for one minute, let alone the twelve night hours as a service from veterinary surgeons. Practices offering that type of service would be out of business very rapidly.

***

Introduction

By 1995, after much agonising, I had completed the sale of my business but stayed on for a time as a non–executive partner. It was not always easy being in the back seat, and when I got the chance and the offer of a job I went to Hong Kong to live and work (more later!) where I did my share of being on call. It was not very onerous as a nurse would take the duty phone and filter the calls, and if I didn't want to go out, or couldn't go out, she would she would send the emergency to the 24 hour clinic – sorted!

***

When I came back to Norfolk to live and resume my veterinary life in the UK, my first weekend on call was not too busy initially due to a football international being screened on terrestrial TV. It was mostly female callers (who were not watching the football) phoning to ask how to remove ticks from their dogs. Had they never heard of Frontline? – Not one of them. My mood lightened a little when a tick enquiry lady told me I sounded like Ewan McGregor. Modest as ever I admitted to a passing resemblance. Well we do come from the same part of the world, and if nothing else it made me laugh.

Things got a bit more serious with the next call when I was asked to see a rabbit with an eye discharge. Thinking it might possibly be myxomatosis I agreed to meet the owners and the rabbit at the clinic. The rabbit was called Fifi and was brought in by a young lad and his girl friend. The eye discharge turned out to be nothing too serious – just conjunctivitis but as the couple left the youth, as a 'by the way,' asked me to look at two cysts at the rabbit's rear end, about which they were worried. I dutifully turned Fifi over to have a look to see two very large not cysts but testicles.After giving the blushing boyfriend an anatomy lesson they hurriedly renamed the rabbit Fred.

I arranged to castrate him (the rabbit - not the boyfriend) the following week.

Vet for Hire

Later the same evening I saw an elderly Jack Russell that was very lame as a result of being chucked in a river by his owner.

The owner quickly explained that she did this all the time in the summer when it was hot to allow the dog to cool off after a walk. There were no obvious fractures and I thought the old boy must have pulled a muscle while struggling to get out of the water and up the river bank. While it was easily treated and the dog was soon feeling more comfortable, I couldn't help feeling the wrong animal had been ducked in the water.

The night ended at 2.00am when I was called out to see a three year old neutered male cat called Tom. His owners described him as being in a lot of pain and it sounded to me as if he might have a blocked bladder. This is usually an emergency situation requiring urgent treatment. As I drove to the clinic I spent some time wondering, as I was still the new 'boy,' where I might find the urinary catheters and speculating who would be the nurse on duty that I might have to disturb.

Tom turned out to be a long haired ginger cat, the 'baby' of a young couple who were convinced their pet was very sick. To be fair Tom was giving forth a very convincing 'yowl' in his carrier basket as he arrived. Palpation of his abdomen revealed a very empty bladder (phew, the relief!), so that was not the cause of his pain. He was, however, very constipated. The examination along with a temperature check was enough for Tom to pass a very hard lump of poo, whereupon he went back into his basket with a smile on his face and promptly fell asleep. "For this relief much thanks and good night," seemed to be his attitude. He wasn't paying the bill for a past midnight consultation and some laxative. The owners were pleased that in the end the condition was not too serious and paid up graciously. I only wish I could have got to sleep as quickly as the cat when I eventually drove back home.

Introduction

Of course most out of hour emergency call outs are genuine. There have been occasions since that inaugural weekend on my return to Norfolk that have tested my patience, but also my clinical and client handling skills. After being in practice for many years there are situations and conditions that are all too familiar, but just now and again you also encounter something which you have never before come across.

It was again an evening call, this time to see a Burmese cat. The owner asked to be seen as his daughter's cat seemed to be in pain. The Burmese was presented as slightly hunched up, miserable, and drooling slightly from the mouth. Under the watchful eye of both father and daughter, I opened the cat's mouth to have a look. The mouth and tongue seemed quite normal, but he had a cracked upper left canine tooth, and the right canine was missing completely. I treated the cat conservatively with antibiotic and a pain killing injection and put him back into the basket while I talked about having him in the next day to do the necessary dental work.

While we were preoccupied with doing this the cat suddenly – and frantically – started clawing at his mouth with his front paws. Before I noticed and got him out of the basket he had managed to completely shred his tongue into at least three different pieces with his long and vicious front claws. Blood was pouring from his mouth and it was quite frankly a horrifying sight. I have seen animals paw at their mouths before, but never in this frantic way, and never to inflict such damage. I quickly sedated him and he went quickly off to sleep which allowed me to fit a buster collar around his head to stop him doing any more damage when he woke up. It was by now quite late and I thought it best for the owner and his by now distraught daughter to go home. I hospitalised the cat until morning. I was very relieved that the cat had done the damage while the clients were present in the clinic and not in the car on the way home. It meant we could deal with it immediately, and it also saved me a difficult phone call and explanation.

Vet for Hire

It was my colleague Ann Hemming who reminded me the next morning about Feline Orofacial Pain Syndrome in Burmese cats. The Feline Advisory Bureau (FAB) had an excellent article on the subject written by Clare Rusbridge. The article described an acute trigeminal neuralgia with oral pain as a precipitating factor. She described the exaggerated licking and chewing movements, and the pawing at the mouth with severe tongue mutilation which had been typical with my case.

I, meanwhile, had to make a more immediate decision regarding the tongue. Did I try and suture what was left of the tongue or go for partial amputation? In the end I decided that some tongue was better than no tongue at all, and I patched it up as best I could with soluble vicryl sutures before removing the broken tooth and the root on the other side which had been the initial cause of the cat's demented behaviour. While he was under the anaesthetic I fitted a nasal gastric tube to make feeding easier and bandaged the front feet with the stickiest, oldest Elastoplast possible. I did this because when he awoke from the initial sedation he had managed to dislodge the drip in his front leg, remove the buster collar and get rid of the normal Vet Wrap bandages he had on his feet.

The next few days turned out to be quite eventful. The cat was proving to be quite a character. He was called Malkin and he wanted as much fuss as possible, but any attempt to touch his head or look in his mouth was liable to set off a spasm of wanting to claw his mouth. This was despite having a constant diet of painkillers which seemed to have only a very limited effect. Valium was more useful to keep him settled and it was while still under the effect of that drug that he seemed, after two days, to turn the corner and made a valiant attempt to eat for himself. Valium has a known side effect of encouraging cats that are reluctant feeders to eat, but it must have been difficult for him. His tongue was still very swollen and painful, but it meant that we could dispense with the feeding tube.

Introduction

Malkin was in the hospital for three weeks. The tongue healed well, but it will be forever forked and hanging to the right side of his mouth. He began to eat well of his own volition (without the aid of valium) when the swelling reduced, and was soon without the buster collar which he had much resented. We did not dare to remove the foot bandages for the first ten days as he was still trying to paw his mouth.

About five days before he was due to go home we tried him again without the foot bandages. We had managed to find and fit soft plastic nails that were glued over his own front nails. These were originally designed to stop cats scratching furniture. Originally a Japanese invention, they now came in a variety of colours so you could colour co-ordinate your cat with your furniture, mood or dress! It was still a scary time as we all knew the risks. If he self-mutilated again he would probably have to be put down as at home continual supervision was just not possible. He was eating well and did not resent the new fashion accessory on his feet.

He went home a very happy cat and his teenage owner and her father were very glad to see him restored to seeming good health. I did make sure that both owners were in no doubt that Malkin may at any time relapse again into self-harm if he was stressed in any way. Even a simple vaccination or being held to look into his mouth might be enough to trigger another episode.

Malkin went home on an evening when I just happened to be on call again. The pager rattled my bedside table at 2.30am. My first wakening thought was "Oh no, it must be Malkin," but it wasn't. It was a lady who rang to ask me how she could get her seven week old Westie puppy to go to sleep as all it wanted to do was play and she wanted to go to bed. My relief that it wasn't my self-mutilating Burmese meant that she didn't get the sort of answer her call deserved. It's all part of the life I lead as a 'Vet for Hire.'

Chapter Two
A Backward Glance

Ocassionally I am asked about the history of my profession, and veterinary practice in general. My knowledge of the subject was fairly abysmal, and it was enough to trigger some research which I found fascinating, but I needed a reference point from which to start. Most species of animals had been hunted by man as a source of food for hundreds of thousands of years. I needed to look at animals from the time when they stopped being prey and started to become useful in other ways.

According to archaeologists dogs were the first animals to be domesticated. This happened in the Middle East about 10,000BC. Cattle, sheep, goats and pigs were the first farmyard animals to be 'tamed.' This occurred about 7,000BC. They had been hunted for meat from the dawn of time by primitive man until someone realised how much more convenient it would be to catch and tame them. They then became a much easier source of food with less effort required. Exploiting animals as beasts of burden and for milk, wool and dung came later.

Cats were different again as they have always tended to be solitary creatures, fiercely territorial and bonded to people's houses rather than to the people themselves. Their habit of rubbing against human legs is not a show of affection but a way of transferring their smell onto an 'owner' – it is simply a way of including the owner within the cat's territory. They became very useful for keeping mice and rats away from grain stores and domestic dwellings and the Egyptians found them to be so valuable in this respect they made them Gods.

Domesticated horses, although tamed much earlier (probably around 8,000BC), did not appear in any great numbers until around 2,000BC, and there is little doubt that methods of horse training and livestock control in general originated in Persia (Iran), Iraq, Egypt and Greece. It is very likely that early medical treatments began around the same time too.

The first veterinary document that we know about relates to treating cattle but there is little doubt that other domestic animals would have been treated in a similar manner. The document is written on papyrus and it exists only as a few fragments which is not surprising as it is dated according to most authorities around 1900 BC. The writing describes three cases in a rational manner much as a modern vet or scientist would. The disease described is recognised now as cattle plague or severe respiratory infection. The treatments too were rational for the time with no resorting to magic or superstition.

This included bleeding (only discounted in recent times), cold water applications (still used) and the use of vegetable oil (still used). It is not certain whether there were veterinarians as such but tomb inscriptions from the time refer to priests with a special knowledge and understanding of animal diseases.

In the time of Babylon in Iraq, the second greatest culture of the Middle East, veterinary practice certainly seemed to exist but I doubt that it actually flourished. The fee structure was appalling. A code stipulated that a 'doctor' of cattle or donkeys must be paid one sixth of a shekel of silver if successful in treating a wound but if not, and the animal died, then the vet would have to pay a fourth of its value to the owner! Some of my Fen farming clients would have loved that arrangement I'm sure but it's hardly a recipe for a thriving veterinary business.

***

I used to look after pigs for a March man called Jim Upton. He reckoned that he shouldn't have to pay for animals that died after treatment. I agreed with him so long as he agreed with me that I should be paid double for those that lived. Strangely

Vet for Hire

enough he didn't take me up on the deal. I would have seen a big increase on his monthly bill!

It was a Roman called Marcus Terentius Varro who described the best of Greek agriculture and veterinary practice. He called Greek vets horse doctors or 'hippiatroi' and claimed that the diseases of horses were as numerous as those of humans. Aristotle made reference to the work of Democritus, perhaps the foremost Greek philosopher before Socrates, much of which has been lost, and we know that he studied anatomy, pathology and physiology. He described pulpy kidney disease of sheep and enterotoxaemia. It is claimed that Democritus exerted a very extensive indirect influence on the development of veterinary medicine which some claim has lasted more than two thousand years.

It is certain that Greek veterinary surgeons were highly esteemed by the Romans. A vet called Eutychos had a title 'Veterinary to the Romans.'

The romanised Greek Apsyrtus was chief veterinary officer to Emperor Constantine's army. There can be no doubt that vets were vital to the Roman army to keep horses and mules healthy and mobile and the great Roman vets who came after owed much to their earlier Greek counterparts.

Publius Vegetius Renatus (Vegetius for short) was a Roman from a good family who loved horses and produced a compilation of work on the diseases of horses and mules. He borrowed from every publication of his time and it is from him that we get an idea of the attitude the Romans had to their horses and veterinary medicine. It seems for the most part that animals were regarded as essential tools of warfare and were looked after as well as possible. Not to do so would have been a waste of resources. That said many cruel practices did occur. You only have to look at many of the Roman bits that have survived to see this. Some severe bits were quite capable of breaking an animal's jaw if full force was applied. Operations such as castrations would, of necessity, be done under restraint. This meant that the animal would be cast to the ground with ropes and its legs tied before any operation. It sounds very cruel but in an age before anaesthetics humans suffered in much the same way when operations were performed. Hopefully though human castrations were few and far between.

'Veterinari' and 'mulomedica,' mostly slaves and of no social significance whatever, were probably just grooms. If the vet was not Roman but not a slave either he was entitled to a rank in the army and could hope to gain citizenship when he had done his time. A few would be high ranking officers and would form part of the staff of the headquarters. Vegetius robustly defends the art of veterinary medicine – it was not, he claimed, a vulgar occupation but ranked with that of a physician. He was said to be the first to report that old adage: "The animal cannot express himself, whereas man can describe his symptoms." How often have I heard that said in so many different ways today. He also complained of treatments costing more than the animal's value and that too would strike a chord with many modern farmers and practice principals. Roman vets used bleeding and cautery as a common form of treatment and the use of both methods, especially cautery, has only just been stopped. Indeed, there are still a few vets who consider cautery ('firing' where hot irons are used to cause the scarring of damaged tendon tissue) as a way to promote the healing and strengthening of tendons.

No modern vet would dispute the Roman method of treating a horse's foot that has developed an abscess. It was very effective. This was to open the source of the infection with a knife and allow it to drain. The foot then had to be kept very clean and covered with a variety of dressings which would sterilise and poultice at the same time by drawing the infection out of the foot. The Romans used oil of roses, vinegar, hot wine and salt to treat the feet and get the Roman war horse

Vet for Hire

back into fighting fettle just as soon as possible.

Castration of Roman cavalry horses was not a common practice. As now one of the reasons for castrating was to make the animal more docile and easier to handle. As a general rule race horses and cavalry mounts were not castrated for a very good reason. A cavalry soldier wanted a fiery, aggressive horse that would positively help him fight the enemy or win races. They needed an animal with lots of testosterone, plenty of attitude and no fear.

The method Roman vets used to castrate was very similar to that used in the Fens where I began my veterinary career (although we did use sedative and anaesthetic). After the animal had been immobilised with ropes and the initial incision made with a knife, metal pincers much like large forceps would have been used to stop the bleeding.

Farm livestock, being more docile when younger, were dealt with in a very different way. Calves were castrated by compressing the neck of the scrotum with a small band of cut fennel, much like the rubber bands that are used today on calves and lambs with the same outcome. It's quick and easy.

Other more difficult operations were carried out too. Eye surgery is described for in-turned eye lids (*entropian* – a very common congenital condition) and also the removal of cataracts. Unfortunately no information survives about how they kept the animal still for such a delicate operation. It is a known fact that surgeons at that time liked to keep their trade secrets so that other professionals could not benefit commercially from another's expertise.

After the fall of the Roman Empire there is no written documentation of any veterinary activity throughout the Dark Ages. Most historians believe that the science of veterinary medicine must have continued in some form or other, and many believe that most of it was based on the work of Vegetius.

It was only at the beginning of the sixteenth century that anatomy and then pathology were studied as a science, mainly in Italy and France. Progress was slow during the next two hundred years and it took a natural disaster in France to stimulate a necessity for a rebirth of veterinary medicine.

It has been estimated that about half of all French livestock died between 1710 and 1770 due to a variety of little understood epidemics. The main disease was thought to be *Rinderpest* which now only tends to appear in Africa.

These problems stimulated a far sighted Louis XV to found the first veterinary school in the World at Lyons. This proved so successful that another was soon opened in Paris. Within a few years veterinary schools had been opened in most major European countries and by the end of the eighteenth century the European Continent was positively bristling with them.

***

England was not far behind and a school of veterinary medicine was established in London in 1791. Scotland was for once out of step with the rest of Europe as it was not until 1823 that William Dick, the son of a farrier, set up the first veterinary school in Edinburgh. I graduated at the 'Dick Vet' less than 150 years later in 1967.

A contemporary description by James Castley of Dick's lecture theatre in Clyde Street is worth a mention: "Skeletons of all descriptions, 'from a child's shoe to a jack boot' - from a horse to an ape, not ranged in 'regular order all of a row', but standing higglety pigglety, their ranks having been broken by the professor's table, and their heads looking in all directions, as if thrown together by chance. Over the professor's 'devoted head' is seen suspended a portion of inflated and injected

Vet for Hire

intestine, with its mesenteric expansion dangling in the air, something like a lure for flies; whilst all around the room, and especially in the corners, are heaped together vast quantities of diseased bones, and other preparations, seemingly without order, and without arrangement. Here we see no numbered specimens - no classification of morbid anatomy - no description book - all of which would tend to give the collection a pretty effect. Yet the lecturer has not only sufficient, but abundance for his purpose: his table is always covered with choice preparations. That portion of the house which is set apart for the audience … is fitted up with rough deal planks, set upon as rough props; the seats rising tier above tier, until your head touches the top of a very dark coloured ceiling."

By the time I attended lectures in Summerhall the anatomical props had all gone but I do recognise the seating arrangement of tier upon tier of uncomfortable wooden planks filled with keen young vet students. In my year we had only six women and I think fifty men. Now the ratio is entirely the other way around. Modern lecture theatres with comfortable upholstered seating and power point computer generated aids to learning are far removed from conditions in the past. I'm sure the likes of William Dick would have relished these more modern conditions and the technology now employed.

Around 1769 the British Army Board of General Officers decided in their collective wisdom to call physicians who attend animal's veterinary surgeons to distinguish them from human surgeons. Previously vets had been called farriers as it was mostly farrier related work they were doing. Previous to that in the days of chivalry they were sometimes called Marshals and before that in the Roman era Medicina Veterinaria.

Slowly the change from animal 'doctoring' and farriery was accomplished as knowledge increased and animals began to be treated in a more rational and scientific manner. By the end of the nineteenth century persons who had obtained a diploma in veterinary medicine were qualified to practice the veterinary art. No longer would treatments be based on folklore and witchcraft. A good example of an old method was the treatment for constipation in cattle. A lively trout would be procured from a nearby stream and pushed down the animal's throat. The idea was that it would swim its way though any blockage and a speedy relief would ensue. I suspect that any cure achieved was due solely to the fright the cow received when being held and drenched with the unlucky trout.

This is not to say that everybody working as a vet was trained and qualified. The town of March was fairly typical of its time. It was, and still is, a small market town in the Cambridgeshire Fens. The first qualified vet to work in the town was John Albert Clarke. He came to March unqualified. He worked for a time as an unregistered vet then went to the London School of Veterinary Medicine from where he graduated after 3 months' training in April 1877. I inherited one of his books that was still in the surgery when I took over the practice. The description of the many illnesses and diseases in the book are easy to follow and understand but the 'recipes' or treatments are often very strange but many are sensible and, as was typical of the books of the time, each treatment was guaranteed a success. This however was probably due to the fact that many animals with illness will get better given time, and those that don't can't talk about it! Mr Clarke married a local girl, a farmer's daughter, and became a farmer himself and his great grandson still farms locally.

His successor in March was a remarkable man. He was Herbert Henry Truman (H. H.) He was born in 1869, graduated from London in 1892 and began work in March in 1896. He too married a local girl and lived to a ripe old age, dying in 1956. He was hugely respected by the local community being a magistrate for thirty two years and Chairman of the local NFU for almost as long. He was largely responsible for the introduction of the Percheron horse to England after the First World War. These animals were especially useful as draught

Vet for Hire

and plough horses. They were large and powerful with good temperaments and did not have feathers down the back of their legs (ie. long hair!) The legs were much easier to keep clean compared to the Shire horses they replaced on many farms as they were much less likely to get skin problems such as Mud Fever which causes lameness. As recognition for this work with Percherons in 1925 the French Government awarded Mr Truman the Chevalier du Merit Agricole.

H. H. Truman's veterinary assistant for many years was Andrew Quarrie Hall, an Edinburgh graduate. It seems he did much of the work for H. H. over the years but was rewarded in the end. Mr Truman gave him the Chatteris practice. He lived at the Moorings in Chatteris and he too died in 1956 when his business reverted back to March. Another practice incorporated into the March set up was owned by an eccentric Irishman called Ernest Wardrop, another Edinburgh graduate. He was very keen on trotting horses and greyhounds and had a thriving farm practice. He died in 1949 aged 72.

Ayrshire born W. A. Noble (Alec) qualified from Glasgow in July 1942 and moved to the Cambridgeshire Fens to take over from Mr Truman after a short stint at Long Sutton where he met his wife Mary (another farmer's daughter). It was he who was the driving force behind the Practice to which I was appointed as a salaried vet. It was a very mixed practice mostly concerned with farm and horse work but also as the years went by with an increasing number of small animal patients. The Practice in March was my first job and it was my intention to stay for a year but the Fens seeped into my soul like a mist on a spring morning and I stayed for well over thirty years. I became, in time, the sole owner of the March Practice but I had a travel bug I needed to feed. When the opportunity arose I sold the business and eventually left to live and work for a time in Hong Kong. I did not realise it at the time as it was my intention to return and resume my life in March, but it was the end of my career in a farm practice.

Chapter 3
Mistakes! I've made a Few

But there again - don't we all. I have over the years been involved with the rescue of many animals from water filled rivers and dykes. Mostly this has been with the assistance of the local fire brigade who are always happy to turn out and render whatever help is required. It has been mostly horses that seem to get into trouble, probably these days because there are far more horses in fields in the Fens than cattle. The Cambridgeshire Fens must have a higher ratio of waterways to land than any other part of the country and they are mostly drainage channels with steep banks. They are necessary as without them most of the fen would be under water. Apart from isolated pockets of higher ground on which most of the towns and villages are built, the fenland countryside is below sea level and drainage has to be highly organised and managed to avoid catastrophic flooding. A good example of this is the surgery car park in March which is seven feet below sea level and suffered very bad flooding when a drain became blocked through bad maintenance. Many of these drains and dykes are unfenced – mostly I suspect due to the expense involved in erecting a barrier and maintaining it. This often means that livestock do have access to waterways with sometimes tragic consequences.

The last rescue in which I was involved had just such a sad outcome. The horse had been in the river for some time and was exhausted before I arrived. Already on the scene, the fire brigade only had fire hoses with which to try and extricate the mare, and it was just not working. I only had my trusty lasso which I had used on other occasions to successfully pull horses

Vet for Hire

from drains. This time I attached the rope while a couple of men kept the animal's head from sinking below the water. The animal was half way out and up the steep banking when my rope broke. I had not noticed it had become weakened and frayed in one section. I could have – should have – tried to attach a fire hose around the mare's chest to give extra assistance in lifting but did not. When the rope broke the horse slipped back into the dyke and died.

The owners never did forgive me for the horse's death, but more importantly I have never really forgiven myself. With foresight I could have done things differently and just might have saved her. What is important when a tragedy like that happens is to learn from it. Fencing rivers to stop livestock from falling in is as important as making sure your equipment is in good condition. Had my lasso not broken at the vital moment the mare might possibly have survived.

***

Every professional person, whether a doctor, dentist, solicitor, vet or any other person dealing with the general public, needs to have professional indemnity insurance. As vets we have the Veterinary Defence Society (VDS) which is another name for an insurance company. Every vet or veterinary practice has this insurance and it is very important for peace of mind. You almost certainly cannot get through a relatively long career without a client with a grudge wanting to sue you or your business, whether it is justified or not.

I have had reason to be grateful to the VDS on two occasions. Most equine practices have horse dealers on their client list. These are people whose business it is to buy and sell horses and ponies and they can sometimes be difficult. This particular lady I had known for about eighteen months and, although I knew her to be a bit volatile we managed to get along reasonably well.

Mistakes!

She called the practice at about 6.00am when it was already daylight with a little light mist over the Fen. It was an emergency as her mare was foaling and the foal was stuck about half way out. The duty vet responded immediately and drove with all haste along the bumpy Fen road next to deep waterways and got to her premises within half an hour of the callout which was a very speedy response from bed to arrival at the yard. He delivered the now dead foal and the client was very upset. She could not understand why he did not have oxygen in the back of his car as she was convinced the youngster could have been resuscitated had he arrived with the relevant equipment.

I saw her later in the day to sympathise with her on her loss. It is always very sad to lose a youngster at birth but I could not agree that the practice was in any way liable or responsible. Not even the highest powered equine practices in Newmarket ever carried oxygen in a car, and in addition the foal had been dead for at least fifteen minutes before my vet arrived.

The upshot of it all was that the lady in question decided to sue as was her right. I phoned the VDS who immediately took the case on board and tried to put my mind at rest.

The claims officer (a vet with legal training) took all the relevant details and let me know a few days later that the VDS would vigorously fight my corner as they did not believe my client had a justified grievance.

The worry dragged on for months as legal matters often do and the case was scheduled for court at the end of September. I had already booked a holiday in Greece but was due back midweek and the case was due to be heard on the following Monday. The VDS had arranged many professional witnesses at great cost who were happy to appear for us, but nonetheless I really did not enjoy my holiday knowing my day in court was imminent. On the Friday before the case was heard it was discovered that the lady in question, unknown to me,

Vet for Hire

was trading under two very different names and had already been declared bankrupt. This meant that her petition failed immediately and was dismissed by the judge. It was relief all round but I couldn't help feeling it had all been a very unnecessary exercise and no, I never did any more work for her!

The other time I was glad to have VDS was when I was asked to pregnancy test between fifty and sixty cows and heifers on Whittlesey Wash for a dealer who was not a client, who had just bought the animals as all 'in calf.' It was a hot but pleasant day and all the animals were going to be first time calvers. The facilities were good with a stockade, a race and a cattle crush where the animals could be penned individually. The only facility that was lacking was electricity so I could not use my ultra sound pregnancy detector which gives a visual image of the various stages of gestation.

Most pregnancy testing is done manually with the hand and arm inside the animal's rectum. Through the rectal wall it is relatively easy to palpate both uterus and ovaries if the animal is not pregnant. If the cow or heifer is heavily pregnant the uterus falls into the abdomen and it and the ovaries cannot be reached at the halfway stage of pregnancy. At this point if I'm not sure I would normally reach for my scanner and this would invariably show the pregnancy on the screen but I could not use it due to the lack of electricity and consequently had to say when I could not feel anything that, on the balance of probability, the animal was probably in calf.

I completed the task and thought no more about it until a few months later when the dealer phoned to complain that five out of the fifty plus heifers I had examined and pronounced to be pregnant were not. When they did not produce a calf they were examined by two other vets and were found to be 'free martins.' Free martins are twin females born with a male sibling. They are unable to breed as their uterus and ovaries have not developed properly, which is why I could not detect them per rectum and had wrongly concluded that they must be in calf.

The dealer had bought the animals from a farmer who must have known the animals were incapable of breeding but had said nothing. Now I was being sued. The VDS were very sympathetic but in the circumstances felt they had no option but to pay up. The inflated figure that was claimed was negotiated downwards by at least fifty percent but it was a salutary lesson.

If I had been anything other than a dour (lapsed) Presbyterian Scot then I sometimes think that I should have adopted St Jude as my patron saint. He is the patron saint of lost causes and there have been many occasions when he might have been invoked, and may even have got some credit when a cause or disaster was sometimes recovered.

***

One of the nightmare situations which most large animal vets dread is the patient, be it a horse or a cow, that cannot for whatever reason get to its feet, stand and walk. There are times when just a little help is all that is required such as a stimulant or a pain killing injection but in many cases this is just not enough and lifting equipment is required.

It is quite common after a foaling or a calving that the mother may have difficulty in rising. This is often due to the foetus being oversized for the birth canal, or sometimes the offspring is coming the wrong way as in a breech birth. The result can be muscle damage, pain and, sometimes crucially, bruising of the vital obturator or sciatic nerves that control the hind quarters. Very often with a bit of rest, treatment and encouragement the mother will stand and all will be well.

Vet for Hire

The first time I encountered just such a scenario in a horse was after I was called to a mare at about 10.30 one evening. She was on her side in a loose box with a dead foal half protruding from her birth canal. The local 'horse expert' had been trying all evening to deliver the dead foal without success and had the good sense to depart the scene before I arrived, but I knew who he was alright!

The mare was totally exhausted, having been pulled about and rolled from side to side in an effort to dislodge the foal. All she needed was to have a reasonable amount of extra lubrication applied all the way around the dead foetus and in the vagina. In a normal birth this is supplied naturally but with the foal being dead everything had dried up. With the obstetrical lubrication supplied from a plastic bottle and applying the right amount of traction in the right direction from a calving machine which I always carried in the car for emergencies, the birth was accomplished within five minutes. I could not help thinking and saying to the clients that if I had been called earlier then the foal may have been alive and the mare would not be in such a bad way. She was quite unable to get to her feet. After I examined her I knew that, although her hind quarter nerves may be bruised they were still working as she was able to respond to painful stimulus. Pressure applied to her hind feet with a hoof tester made her try and kick. I made her comfortable for the night with a couple of injections and propped her up on her chest. When I left she was eating hay and I was reasonably hopeful that after a good night's rest she would be on her feet by morning.

No such luck! Morning came around and I made her my first visit. She was just as I had left her. She was not in the least interested in standing despite some vocal and physical encouragement which in less severe circumstance often works. It is one of those irrefutable facts of life that if a large animal doesn't get up within the first twenty four hours of a difficult obstetrical procedure then the chances are very high that the mother will not walk again.

I needed to enlist some extra help. At one time most large animal practices would have a lifting harness to cope with the high percentage of equine work, but not any more, although I knew where I could borrow a set. An old vet in a neighbouring practice, Sam Poles, still had the right equipment in reasonable working order and was very willing to let us borrow it. While I was getting this organised the horse's owner phoned the local fire brigade to explain and enquire if they could assist. They were delighted to come out and were on the scene before I got back with the hoisting gear. The senior officer was directing his men to support the stable roof with jacks as he had correctly worked out that the beams alone would not support the weight of the mare. She was going to be lifted by a pulley once the harness had been fitted, which was about to be placed over a convenient overhead rafter.

When everything was in place and with the harness around the mare, the pulley was attached. Six burly firemen grabbed the rope and up she went. As her body left the ground the horse began to feel her feet and tried to walk. Fortunately she was prevented from doing this by her restraints and by the rest of the team gathered around her. Had everything not been correctly in place she would have crashed to the ground and that would have been disastrous – almost certainly she would have had to be put down on welfare grounds. Giving her lots of time, encouragement and support she was eventually able to stand more or less on her own. The fire team stayed with her most of the day, sustained by an almost continuous supply of tea and bacon butties just in case there were any further problems. They were an immensely cheerful and happy team and without a doubt they had saved the horse's life.

She stayed in the harness for over a week until I was as sure as I could be that she would be able to walk and turn unaided. Her foal had died but at least she was eventually fit and well.

Vet for Hire

Her owner very sensibly listened to my advice and never tried to put her in foal again.

Not all cases end quite so happily. A colleague was called in the early hours of the morning to a very similar situation. This time, however, the owners had not delayed in getting professional help. After a bit of difficulty a good live foal was delivered and all seemed well. The mare was very tired but as she tried to get to her feet she fell awkwardly. The vet stayed with her most of the night, trying to make her comfortable and making sure the foal got colostrum by milking the mother as she lay on the ground.

By morning it was all too apparent that she was not going to get up unaided. A call went out again to a different fire brigade (we were in another part of the county) and they responded with the same speed as the first unit.

The officer in charge went to Cambridge to borrow the necessary lifting harness and while he was doing this (he had to travel over thirty miles there and back) his men set about taking the roof off the stable as the rafters were too low and not strong enough to support the animal hanging in slings. A JCB digger was borrowed from somewhere, and by the time I arrived to relieve the exhausted vet all I had to do was organise the fitting of the harness around the patient.

The mare was quite distressed and tending to throw her herself around a bit. I did not want to give her a sedative to calm her down as this might make it more difficult for her to stand unaided. She had already been given all the pain relief that was possible. Instead a firewoman who owned her own horse was delegated to hold the animal's head to try and comfort her and keep her quiet. She collected quite a few bruises for her pains as the mare continued to toss about in her futile attempts to get up.

Mistakes!

When at last everything was ready and in position, the bucket of the JCB was positioned above the horse where the roof had been. The hook of the sling was attached and the order given to the driver to lift away slowly and carefully.

It worked well! Up the mare went gradually and was supported on all sides by many willing helpers. We tried for some time to get some sort of sensation into her limbs to enable her to stand by herself with support but all to no avail. I was just about to give the order to let her down to rest again for a bit when she died. I had suspected that this was always a possibility given her general condition and the enormous strain her heart was under, but I could tell the fire team were very upset and needless to say the owners were devastated. It was one of those times when, despite everything possible being done. the patient still died and St Jude was conspicuous by his absence.

At least I am happy to report that the foal, a strong healthy colt, did very well with a foster mother. I am sure he will have no memory of the trauma of his birth or of his mother who died giving him life. But we who were there for all or part of the time of her great struggle to survive will remember the mare's courage and tenacity which in the end was not enough.

***

In the course of my large animal work I encountered and attempted to treat many more cows than horses that were unable to stand up after giving birth. These were mostly for the same reasons that mares could not get up – damage at parturition – but cows also have an extra category. Vets have called it 'Downer Cow Syndrome.'

My favourite story concerned a fairly old Aberdeen Angus cow which I diagnosed as a'Downer Cow.' She was owned by a smallholder who, along with his wife, still farmed even

Vet for Hire

though they were both well into their eighties. The cow had a normal calf about two weeks before she lay down and refused to get up. When this happens to cows after calving it is mostly due to Milk Fever. Like many diseases it is badly named. The patient does not have a fever and it is not infectious. It is a metabolic disorder which causes the cow to have low calcium levels in the blood stream. The net result of this is that the patient gets very sleepy and lies down. They can on occasions look almost dead. However usually giving a calcium solution by a drip into the jugular vein can cause the patient to rise like Lazarus. This can be very satisfying and good for the veterinary ego but occasionally, even although the diagnosis has been correct, the cow steadfastly refuses to get to her feet. This can be due to a number of reasons; muscle and pelvic damage if she fell down or just sheer laziness. However, as with horses, leaving a cow to lie for a number of hours is not a good option as muscles become cramped and lose the power to work in a normal way.

This was just such an occasion. The cow herself looked very bright and happy after treatment for Milk Fever but twenty four hours later she was still recumbent on a thick bed of straw.

The lifting apparatus for cows is very different to horses. For many years we used a piece of kit known as a Bagshaw Hoist. It's a metal clamp which is fitted on either side of the animal's protruding pelvic bones then usually connected to a pulley system in the roof. Horses, once hoisted with the lifting harness, will stand quite happily for days on end as they can sleep on their feet. Cows don't and will mostly just slump into the harness and get bloated. Cows connected to a Bagshaw Hoist can only be elevated for a short period of time before they have to be allowed to lie down again and the hoist removed. To do otherwise would cause huge pressure sores to the animal and considerable extra discomfort. Usually, providing there is no serious damage to the cow such as a broken pelvis, they only need to be lifted on two or three occasions after which they will be able to stand and move unaided. This particular black cow required lifting for over two weeks before she finally got the message and stayed on her feet. This in itself was quite a problem as the old couple needed help three to four times every day to lift the uncooperative animal. Friends, relations and any other willing soul within a five mile radius were roped in to help. The farmer's wife was a brilliant baker and maker of cups of tea which kept the volunteers happy. However I did think it was reward enough to see the cow happily grazing again in her field by the roadside as I drove past every day.

One of the most bizarre rescues in which I ever took part again concerned a horse. For reasons that were never properly explained at the time a stable had been erected over a cesspit with the manhole cover placed in the centre of the loose box. Most of the time the heavy metal cover was not seen as it was normally covered with bedding and the owners of the animal swore that it was the previous property owners who had erected the building. It was an accident waiting to happen, and it duly did. The round, heavy metal entrance collapsed under the weight of the current occupant (a fifteen hand mare) of the stable and the horse fell hind quarters first into the hole. She was only stopped from disappearing into the depths of the pit by her hips and pelvic bones. When I arrived she was desperately trying to extricate herself from the hole with her front feet, but of course could not use her hind legs as they were dangling uselessly in a very smelly void.

As ever I needed more man power. We needed to demolish the stable as it would be much easier to get all the available help around the animal. We also needed to get a straight up, vertical pull on the animal to have any chance of getting her out. With the building demolished it was easy to get a JCB close with the bucket overhead. Where would we be without the JCB? They seem to be everywhere just when you need one, even in the most remote parts of the Fen. I managed to get a thick strap around her body and it took only a few feet

Vet for Hire

of upwards elevation to get her pelvis clear of the hole and the hind legs followed quite easily. When she was finally out and with the strapping and ropes removed, the mare lay flat out – exhausted, winded and bruised by her ordeal. Thankfully after a few minutes when I propped her onto her chest she was able to get up and walk very stiffly away. She was stinking very badly and so were we all, but it was a small price to pay and I think the owner was only too glad to relocate the stable well away from the cesspit. He was not about to repeat past mistakes. He made the pit safe by putting a few wooden palettes over the entrance hole until he found a new cast iron lid and made it so secure that another animal or person could not be at risk of suffering the same fate.

It was probably the single strangest and thankfully the most successful rescue out of all those in which I have been involved over all my many years as a vet.

Chapter Four
Fat Baby and the Sex Change

I had sold my practices and professionally speaking, although still employed as a consultant, I was now footloose and fancy free. I had previously visited Hong Kong on holiday and had been fascinated by the country and the culture. On my last visit I had been in touch with a colleague who worked in Sai Kung in the New Territories. Lindsay Thomas had worked for me in Wisbech and I had given him a reference when he was offered a job in the Far East. As part of our holiday my wife and I got on a bus and paid him a visit. It was a beautifully warm and sunny Sunday without a trace of the humidity or pollution for which Hong Kong is somewhat notorious. A trip to a beach and a swim was the obvious thing to do. Hong Kong is not all concrete jungle and huge sky scrapers. There is remote tropical jungle, mountains and fabulous beaches, all within easy reach of Victoria and down town Kowloon. We went to the harbour in Sai Kung and boarded a sampan which in about twenty minutes took us to a very hot beach with golden sands. The water of the South China Sea was very warm and inviting. After the beach we had a barbeque at Lindsay's apartment and it had been a thoroughly wonderful day. I mentioned to him that he was doing something I had always wanted to do – namely work abroad. "Well why don't you?" was his reply.

My lame excuse was that I was too old and that no one would want to employ me at my 'advanced age.'

"Don't be silly," came the brisk reply, "You're not too old. Go for it if you want. Why don't you?"

Vet for Hire

And that's how my wife and I came to be landing that following February at a wet and cold Chek Lap Kok, Hong Kong's new international airport. It was not an auspicious start. It was more like the aircraft had taken a wrong turning and we had landed in Edinburgh. Hot, blue skies and balmy South China Sea – I don't think so!

Lindsay's 'why don't you' almost hit me on the very first consultation. I had decided to make my first day of work a Saturday, shadowing and observing him in the consulting room.

A middle aged Chinese couple rushed through the clinic door with a six week old Yorkshire terrier. They did not have an appointment but the puppy was totally collapsed. The husband and wife explained through our nurse interpreter Achee that the dog had been fine the previous evening but they had woken up to find it flat out and unable to lift even its head. The only diagnostic feature from my limited perspective was pupils that were pin point in size. It seemed to be aware of its surroundings and could feel pain when I pinched its toe. It may also have had diarrhoea but we were not sure. Both Lindsay and I suspected some form of poisoning, or even meningitis. We wanted to admit the puppy as it needed to be put on an intravenous drip as soon as possible and we needed to run some diagnostic tests. After this was explained the owners went into a Chinese huddle and asked for time to consider what they wanted to do. They then retreated to the waiting room where animated conversations in Cantonese were conducted with various relatives via mobile phone.

The decision took about twenty minutes while the pup still lay moribund on the consulting room table, unable to move even its tail. If we could not promise to make it better with an injection or two (and we could not do so without making a diagnosis), then they would take it home to allow it to die in peace.

Fat Baby

I was more than a little aghast at this turn of events as the dog disappeared out of the door, never to be seen again, "Welcome," said Lindsay. "Welcome to Hong Kong."

***

Over the years it is inevitable with a memory like mine that most patients and cases are rapidly forgotten, but there are a few animals and conditions I will never forget – ever. Even with the passage of time some animals, because of their personality or the outcome of their individual treatment – good or bad – leave an indelible mark. If a patient dies and, like the horse in the river, their death could have been avoided, it leaves a permanent scar which, even years later, I return to pick at in a mildly masochistic way. Fortunately, for the sake of my sanity, to counterbalance those often miserable negative thoughts I also have many others where a case turned out well despite many difficulties and made me feel that perhaps – on occasion – I may have made a difference after all. In Hong Kong even after a short time I acquired many new patients that were memorable but two in particular will stay with me for life. Fat Baby and Tam Cheung made just such a lasting impression.

One of the many common disorders in Hong Kong, apart from the many tropical and sub-tropical parasitic diseases, is urolithiasis in both dogs and cats. In lay terms this simply means a bladder that is blocked by little stones, crystals or struvite which have precipitated out of the urine and the unfortunate animal is unable to pee normally. I hadn't been in Hong Kong for more than a few weeks before I had unblocked many castrated male cats and carried out four bladder operations on both male and female dogs. This seemed to be many more than I would encounter in a whole year in the UK and I consulted a few colleagues as to why they thought there was such a high incidence of this condition.

Vet for Hire

Opinions seemed to be divided on the main reasons, but two theories seemed to be the most favoured. Castrated male cats are desexed, the expression used in the Far East, when the animal is quite a lot older than six months which is the most likely age for the operation in the UK. The early age for castration in the UK does appear as one of the possible reasons for the illness occurring in Britain but in Hong Kong, as cats mostly come into the clinics to be neutered at around eighteen months old, it would tend to discount early neutering as a reason for the high incidence. Many cats are fed a good quality dry food, however those fed on inferior quality food from market stalls or those with diets supplemented with human or inferior food can experience disastrous results. A bad diet can result in a urinary acid/alkali imbalance which is a likely cause of bladder stones and struvites.

All these thoughts 'crystallised' one evening when Fat Baby (BB) came into the clinic at Tai Wai. He was (and apparently still is) a very fat, neutered Scottish Fold cat. He had a long history of bladder blockages and intimate acquaintance with urinary catheters. This was despite having a very loving owner who was quite adamant that she always fed the correct diet which in theory should stop the bladder urine crystallising or forming plugs of struvite. Well it certainly hadn't worked for Fat BB as the clinical examination did not take too long to reveal that his bladder was once again blocked.

Straining to wee on the consulting table rather gave the game away but I examined him anyway. His bladder was very full, tense and sore, and it is not difficult to imagine just how painful that condition can be.

There was nothing else for it but to resort to catheterising BB yet again under a general anaesthetic. It was only nine months since the last episode. He was duly anaesthetised and the catheter passed into the bladder with great difficulty. The urethra was very blocked and it took about an hour of flushing and suction before the problem was relieved, but as our head nurse (called coincidentally Cat) at Tai Wai said as the urine began to flow freely, "Jeez, does this boy need a sex change!" By this I assumed she meant a perineal urethrostomy. I could only agree. It was self-evident that the cat's urethra – the tube from the bladder through the penis by which the urine is voided – was very narrow and probably scarred and damaged by previous encounters with vets and urinary catheters.

Not to get too technical the operation involves amputating the penis where the urethra is at its most narrow, and fashioning another opening higher up towards the tail where the urethra has a much wider diameter. In essence, if the job is done properly the result is an opening into the urethra that looks like a vulva – hence Cat's very descriptive term 'sex change.'

Cat gave me the third degree. She hadn't known me very long – could I do this operation, had I done it before and would I do it again and to this patient?

The answer to all her questions was 'yes' and I was proposing to do it again to BB. I just omitted to tell her that it was at least ten years since the last time and the outcome, although successful initially, did not last. I was reasonably confident though that all would be well this time. Besides, if I wasn't going to do the operation then the alternative was to put BB to sleep as it was not fair to allow him to continue to suffer in this way. I knew there was an excellent surgical text book in the library which I could use to refresh my memory of the procedure. I also knew that my eyesight, even with my half moon reading glasses, was not as it had been even a few years ago, but there was a very useful piece of kit in the clinic called an Optivisor. This was worn over the face like swimming goggles and magnified the operating field by at least two, which I knew was enough to see both me and BB through the operation.

Vet for Hire

Fat BB and a very worried owner duly turned up the next day. The cat still had his catheter in place and this was important when it comes to the operation for dissecting the penis away from the surrounding connective tissue. Those males among you of a sensitive disposition should probably look away now.

I made an elliptical incision (a 'tear drop') around the scrotum and sheath after placing a pair of Allis (not Alice, which given the procedure might have been more appropriate) tissue forceps on the end of the now redundant penis and catheter. It was then fairly straightforward to reflect the penis first upwards and then down to expose the whole length of the organ. After removing all the muscle attachments I made a longitudinal incision using a very fine scalpel blade along the length of the penile urethra with the catheter still in place. This makes the procedure so much easier.

Up to this point I had managed quite successfully with my ordinary glasses but now I was struggling. I found it impossible to suture the lining of the urethra to the skin without the magnifying optivisor, which is vital for the long term success of the operation. With it attached over my head – a vision which made the nurses giggle uncontrollably – it became quite easy to visualise and suture the necessary parts together using very fine absorbable suture material. I did not want to take these sutures out. They would fall out naturally after a few weeks. The final stage of the operation was to amputate the now defunct and troublesome penis and scrotum and put the final skin sutures in place which left Fat BB looking just like a girl. Maggie, one of the nurses who had helped with the operation, said it looked just like a sex change operation she had watched in Thailand. She said it was on video. I didn't ask for more details in case I got too much information.

Fat BB went home late in the evening the next day, a little uncomfortable but peeing with ease. The owner was pleased, Cat was pleased, and I'm pretty sure BB was alright about it as well, judging by the way he ate his dinner before he left. We had only one minor hiccup.

Two days after the operation the owner phoned to say BB had not passed any urine all day. She brought him from his home twenty kilometres away on the bus in a travel bag. By the time he had reached the clinic he had produced a vast amount of urine, most of which had leaked through the bag and onto the owners lap. Was she upset? Not a bit because her beloved BB was alright. A year later he was still doing OK, although the battle to reduce his weight was not as successful. Since that time in Hong Kong I have done one more sex change operation on another Scottish Fold cat. Sam was turned into a Sammy with equally satisfying results.

As well as being linked to poor diets, the higher incidence of bladder stone problems in dogs may also have been the result of high-rise living. Very many dogs live in skyscraper apartment blocks and are only allowed out twice a day for a walk and a pee if they are lucky! In some cases owners are keeping pets against the landlord's wishes which means the animal has to be smuggled in and out in a shopping bag. Occasionally the only time the dog gets fresh air, apart from that available on a balcony, is when it is time to visit the vet. The likely outcome with so few opportunities to empty the bladder and wildly abnormal lengths of time for urine retention is a much higher risk of minerals precipitating from the urine and stones forming.

All the stones I removed from bladders in Hong Kong dogs were triple phosphates which is the common variety with up to twenty in each bladder at any one time, although one dog had at least fifty by the time I gave up counting. In each case I put the patients onto a diet to prevent the formation of any more crystals or stones and I had no post-op recurrences in all the time I worked in Hong Kong. However, I really did not think client compliance was any better in Hong Kong than in

Vet for Hire

the UK, and as for many the lure of the cheaper market food will always prove all too irresistible.

If Fat BB was a memorable feline case then Tam Cheung was the dog that refused to die, although it might be more accurate to say he simply had the great good fortune to meet people who refused to let him die. He was not very old when our paths crossed – he was about seven months old and had already had five close brushes with the grim reaper that I knew about, and still he lived and breathed (and barked!). As I was making my initial notes about him he was yelling in my ear for more food.

He did not have a great start in life. He was found in a storm drain when he was only a few weeks old along with four litter mates. He should have drowned then like his siblings as that was the obvious intention of the person who threw them into the water. Instead he was found and rescued by Mr Ng whose hobby in life is to rescue canine waifs and strays. Mr Ng is a very busy business man but before he goes to work either in Hong Kong or in China he visits various locations around Sai Kung where experience has taught him he might find dogs in distress. That particular morning followed an evening of heavy rain and Mr Ng knew there was a chance that a stray might have fallen into the rain swollen channel, but even he was not expecting to find Tam Cheung and his siblings floating down the water in a large, black plastic bag.

Under normal circumstances Tam would have drowned or might have been found by other men whose intentions were never fully honourable, especially if you are a dog. Dogs in Hong Kong still get eaten, although it is illegal. Canine kebabs could have been Tam Cheung's fate if found by the wrong people, together with fattening ready for a winter's feast which is the time of year when dogs are more likely to get eaten in the Far East.

Fat Baby

Tam was a fairly non-descript black and tan mongrel with a fairly high percentage of German Shepherd genes and a bark to match. His name means police inspector (or so I was told) as the waterway in which he and his companions were found was very close to the Sai Kung police station and he also had a very nosy disposition. I first met him when he was admitted for castration and a bilateral inguinal hernia repair. Another colleague had already done his routine vaccinations. His operations were straightforward and without incident and I will admit that while he had my full attention for the time he was under my care, I forgot about him as soon as he had vacated the premises.

One Monday evening in August at around about 7.30 just as I was contemplating going home with thoughts of having a large glass of red wine, Tam Cheung was brought back to the clinic. He was totally collapsed and along with him was another equally sick companion. At the time I wasn't sure which dog was going to die first. It seemed to be a close run race and I was uncertain who needed my immediate attention and who could wait a little longer.

Tam's companion was a beagle about nine months old. It was very distressed and breathing as if it had just run a marathon. Its rectal temperature was a very unhealthy 41°C and it was very dehydrated. I decided immediately that it should be first and quickly got a drip into its vein along with some intravenous antibiotic and began treating it for pneumonia, confirmed after listening to its chest.

With that done I turned my attention to Tam Cheung. His gums and eye membranes should have been a healthy salmon pink colour but they were white – literally white, not even magnolia. He was so weak he could only just lift his head. He also had diarrhoea which was black and bloody. When the nurse lifted him onto the table she could feel his distended stomach rattling like a purse full of coins. It took only a

Vet for Hire

moment to decide that if this dog was to have any chance of survival he would have to have a blood transfusion – and quick. As good luck would have it we had another large dog in the kennel registered to Mr Ng. It had come in for a skin condition but as otherwise healthy was an ideal candidate to be a blood donor. It only took a few minutes to get consent to use the dog and harvest enough blood for the transfusion. In the meantime we did run a sample from Tam for a complete blood count and check for blood borne parasites. His packed cell volume (PCV) was less than ten percent. A normal sample would be between thirty five and fifty percent. I assumed, in addition to the foreign objects in his stomach, he must have tick fever as well which is the most common cause of anaemia in the Far East. Despite having difficulty in finding enough red cells in his circulation to have a good look, I thought I could detect enough evidence of Babesia gibsoni to give him the standard treatment of one injection of *Berenil*. This is a drug which is not licensed to treat anything other than cattle elsewhere in the World, but in Hong Kong it is used very safely and successfully for dogs. After this I took an X-ray of his abdomen. It only needed one X-ray plate and one view to display a fine array of stones and nails which Tam must have picked up while foraging. Survival habits learned young are not easily forgotten, even when are being fed well, and there was little to tell how long they had been in the stomach.

It was out of the question to even think of an operation that night. The first priority was to get enough blood into his system to stop him dying if we could. There was an additional risk too – as we could not cross match his blood with the donor he might have an anaphylactic reaction to the donor's blood. But it was a risk we had to take – without the blood transfusion he would die. I left Tam with blood dripping into one vein and saline into the other. I could do no more until the morning. When I arrived the next day he was standing. He had had all the blood and saline overnight and his packed cell volume (PVC) had now gone up to sixteen percent. By seven o'clock in the evening, just twenty four hours after arriving, he was much improved and getting really bright and cheeky. I decided now was as good a time as any to remove his excess baggage.

The operation went well. Tam was very stable under the anaesthetic and gave me no cause for alarm throughout the procedure. I managed to extract all the stones and as it turned out three nails through quite a small hole in his stomach wall. Tam woke up with commendable speed and I heaved a huge sigh of relief. I left him for a second night still on a drip but feeling much better about him. His companion from the previous evening was doing even better and had already gone home.

The next day was my day off but I phoned in to find Tam's condition not improved as I had hoped, but worse. Cavan was the vet in charge for the day. He had monitored his PCV as the hours went by to find by late evening that it had almost dropped to seven percent – even worse than before! There must be something else going on.

He needed to have another blood transfusion from a different donor, despite the terrible risk that it might kill him off completely. He was going to die anyway without it. The black and bloody diarrhoea had come back with a vengeance and he was still obviously bleeding into the bowel. Cavan looked at a wet preparation of the diarrhoea and found hook worms in profusion. This was in spite of a good and properly followed cleansing policy in the kennels and regular deworming.

He should not have had any sort of worm, let alone hook worm, but he did and this and not the foreign bodies must have been the cause of the bloody diarrhoea.

No time was lost in making Tam swallow the appropriate medication and by next morning he again seemed to have turned a corner and was going to live.

Vet for Hire

The following day saw a new dog and a new vet. Lindsay was now in charge and he had little to do apart from monitor Tam's by now excellent progress. He had begun to eat small amounts of food regularly and wanted more. Lindsay considered allowing him to go home but by mid afternoon he took a turn for the worse again. He went very quiet and his abdomen became distended. He was obviously in pain. I was worried when I heard – I was at another clinic – that he might have developed peritonitis from his first operation. However, an X-ray of his abdomen pointed to a different problem altogether.

He needed an operation quickly due to an intussusception caused by one part of his intestine contracting too rapidly and overtaking a less active piece of bowel. The result of this intestinal leapfrogging was a blockage which was why Tam had become very sick again. Fortunately for the dog Lindsay and nurse Achee had been very quick to spot the problem and the operation was straight forward and a complete success.

I returned to find Tam looking amazingly well. His PCV was almost twenty and the diarrhoea had stopped. I kept him in an extra day but by next morning he needed to go home. He was eating ravenously, passing normal poo and needed to be back with his friends. As he left with Mr Ng I reflected on the adage 'never give up on a young animal.' Dogs and cats have strong survival instincts and don't know how ill they are, which probably helps their recovery. They also know nothing of death, leaving us humans to do their worrying for them.

When I went back to Hong Kong to do a locum a year later Mr Ng heard I was in town again and brought Tam Cheung back to see me. "To say thank you," he said.

I hardly recognised him as he had grown into a very large, very active dog. He didn't know me at all. Grateful – I don't think so but I was very pleased to see him.

Chapter Five
Fenland Characters

I have, over many years of working in the Fens of Cambridgeshire, Norfolk and Lincolnshire, seemingly dispensed drugs with one hand and occasionally death with the other. During my travels I have met and in many cases made friends with Fenland farmers and stockmen. Many of these gentlemen were 'individual,' that is to say they had, for the most part, many idiosyncratic tendencies. Every human being is unique but there is no doubting that some are more unique than others. I think it's probably a trait that is common in most parts of the country where people keep livestock. You only have to read the Herriot stories to realise that Yorkshire is overpopulated with 'mad men,' but Fenland over the years has had more than a few characters. Inevitably many of the more colourful clients have been middle aged to elderly, and in the end pen of life from which God tends to draw new recruits.

With each funeral it is often said that 'we will not see his like again' which is true enough, but I have always believed that new individuals are always forming and developing to take the place of those who have passed on. At least I did but now I'm not so sure. Most of the men of whom I shall speak were fashioned by an intimate knowledge of the land they farmed, the landscape they lived in and the animals they reared. Livestock farming is now disappearing at an alarming rate in many parts of the country, and particularly in the Fens where a good living can be had by being an arable farmer. It is a lot less hassle just to grow crops – no unsocial hours except at harvest time and you are insulated from the ravages of the climate and the cold east wind by a warm tractor cab with all mod cons. I would not be surprised if some of the vehicles did not have cappuccino machines and flushing toilets fitted

Vet for Hire

as they seem to have every other modern convenience. It all leads to a much drabber, duller lifestyle which tends to blunt any nascent nonsense that might otherwise have developed if you had been up half the night wrestling with a recalcitrant heifer trying to give birth or dodging the outraged advances of a bad tempered boar trying to attend to his business of impregnating the latest member of his harem.

Welney is my favourite Fenland village. At first sight it's not much to look at and pretty unremarkable. It's built on either side of the Wisbech to Ely road with old and new houses. The church is nineteenth century and attractive enough without being special, and almost next door is a typically Victorian school from which young children still spill out at the end of the school day. For a small village it had three pubs but only one is still serving pints to the locals. The Lamb and Flag is the survivor and as I first knew it did not, like many of its contemporaries, have a proper bar. Customers – locals and visitors alike, sat with their backs to the wall or at tables playing cards or dominoes in a front room which in the winter months housed a large roaring fire. Beer was served in pint jars through a small hatchway in the wall direct from barrels in the cellar. What made Welney unique in my eyes and formed the character of the village and its inhabitants was its situation on the edge of what was and is known as Welney Wash.

On the south side of the village are three parallel rivers. These are the Old and New Bedford (also known as the Hundred Foot) and closest to the village, the Delph. They were all created by a Dutch engineer called Cornelius Vermuyden who was asked in the middle of the seventeenth century by the fourth Earl of Bedford to try and reclaim the Fens from the winter floods which occurred every year and kept the Fens as an almost constant land of marshes, reeds and meres. These rivers have stopped the surrounding Fens from flooding by channelling the extra winter flood water that would otherwise unite the rich farm land quickly with the sea at Kings Lynn.

Fenland Characters

Between the two main rivers is about three quarters of a mile of road and many thousands of acres of rough pasture from Earith upstream to Denver downstream. In the winter this huge area known far and wide as Welney Wash is allowed to fill with excess water which might otherwise flood over the high river banks. The area that is flooded is a fantastic feeding ground for thousands of ducks, geese and swans during the winter months. The RSPB now owns most of the Wash land along with the Wildfowl Trust and migrating swans from the Arctic come every winter to rest and feed. In the summer this land is good rough grazing for livestock and where I have spent many often difficult hours catching and attending to calving cows. Owners who rent the grazing pay shepherds to look after their animals. They in turn call for the vet when treatment is required and any call out to Welney Wash is treated with some trepidation as you know you could be gone for some time. It can be idyllic in the summer on a lovely warm day and the animals contained in large holding pens provide easy access, but in winter when it is empty of treatable animals it can be very bleak, wild and desolate. For quite a few months in the year Welney can be surrounded by thousands of acres of flooded wash land and the road to Ely is impassable and often under a least six feet of water. The boys and often the not so young men in the village would tend to congregate on the bridge when the wash road floods, and if asked were always optimistic about a motorist's chances of getting through the flood waters, thus avoiding the long diversion via Downham Market which would otherwise be required. If a car inevitably gets stuck then a tractor can be summoned to pull the vehicle out – but for a fee of course. If nothing else it paid for a few pints in the Lamb and Flag.

***

Like his father Joe Bedford, Peter, known as 'Pop,' farmed cattle in Welney and did his share of rescuing on the Wash road. Why he was called Pop I have no idea. He never married

Vet for Hire

and as far as I know never had any children and lived with his widowed mother. In the winter months his cows were all housed in yards at his farm in the middle of the village. Calves would be born in the big straw yard from October to March and out on the Wash land in the summer months. Peter did not require the services of shepherds. He looked after his livestock himself summer and winter alike. Apart, that is, from every Saturday when Chelsea played at home when he would travel to Stamford Bridge to watch the home game. Otherwise he rarely ventured out of the village. When he was away Mr Scarff who worked on the neighbouring farm across the road would keep a kindly eye open for any problems. Mr Scarff was especially good at looking after calves. He must have liked youngsters as he had fourteen children of his own, but I digress.

Peter was a genial giant of a man who loved his cows. He would talk to them all the time when he was in the yard, feeding them and giving them fresh bedding. He did have one problem when it came to looking after them. He was very squeamish. This could present quite a problem for the vet – usually me – as if there was any blood or mess to be dealt with Peter just could not cope. His aged mother was more useful. If one of his cows in the yard needed attention or was calving he could just about be relied on to hold the halter at the head end, but asking to pull on a rope to assist with pulling out a calf was a non starter. Even when just positioned at the head end he did faint on a couple of occasions while holding the cow's halter but to give him his due, even unconscious on his back with his eyes shut he still held the rope firmly in both his hands. When the procedure was finished and the calf born he would struggle to his feet with a sheepish grin on his face. He was not alone in this trait as I have known other farmers crash to the ground without warning while assisting with caesareans, and my own father was always reluctant to deal with blood.

Peter would allow some of his cows to give birth on the

Fenland Characters

Wash in the summer, but that stopped after a particularly harrowing episode. A young heifer got into difficulties one evening while it was still light. He summoned help including me. It was immediately apparent that this was not a normal calving. The calf was dead inside the mother, leaving us just two options. One was a caesarean for which she would have to be transported back to the yard. This was not a viable option as transport was not possible from such a remote location. We were miles down the river bank towards Earith and not accessible by vehicle. The other option, as the calf was a bit of a monster and could not be delivered by normal traction, was to cut it up inside the mother; a procedure called embryotomy. This is always a long, drawn out and difficult procedure from which I would receive no help from Peter. It was just as well his friends were around to assist. From time to time he would disappear over the banking towards the river when he couldn't stand it anymore. There was even a worry when he was away for some time that he might have thrown himself into the Old Bedford River as he was blaming himself for the animal's predicament. The calf was eventually delivered in bits and Peter swore that from then on any cows that were heavy in calf would come home for a safer delivery.

Peter also had another defect as far as I was concerned. He had absolute unjustifiable faith in my ability to catch any difficult patient with my lasso. I admit that once or twice I got lucky, which meant he always requested me to attend. It led to a few occasions when it proved impossible to catch the beast and treatment had to be deferred until he was able to get the animal into a pen with the help of many cronies. But he never blamed me for my failures as he reckoned that if I couldn't catch it then nobody could!

He was a man slow to anger but he did have a stubborn streak. One of his non-farming neighbours used to make a nuisance of himself by leaving his car blocking a drove road at the back of Peter's farm. He did it once too often. Peter

Vet for Hire

blocked one end of the drove with his tractor and the other end with a car just as the neighbour was going to work.

He phoned Peter up and asked him very impolitely to move the vehicles so he could get to work.

"Can't do that just at moment," was the reply.

"Why the !*?! not?"

"Avin' me breakfast," came the response.

"How long are you going to be?"

"Can't tell mate, most farmers like me do their business on the phone at breakfast time."

Peter kept him waiting for over an hour before he shifted the tractor and the neighbour was always more careful how he parked his car and never blocked the road again.

Peter died much too young due to a heart attack. A few weeks before he died he had visited his doctor for a check up. On his return he was asked what the doctor had said.

"The doctor said I had not to buy any new shoes."

We took it from that the consultation had not gone well. No one was very sure whether the doctor had actually said it or not, or it was just Peter's way of imparting bad news.

Les Johnson was another of the 'old school' in Welney. He was a short, stout little man and very shy except when he had been in The Three Tuns next to the Delph River, his favourite watering hole. Les always wore a bowler hat when he was out drinking and the angle at which it was tilted gave a fair measure of his inebriation. He was so scared of the phone he would always get someone else to ring for the vet through the day – usually his mother, but at night and after a few pints of Elgoods best bitter he would not only use the phone, he would try and reverse the charges which was never made him very popular.

He kept his pigs at the Suspension Bridge side of the Wash and his sows were, by common consent, the fattest, worst tempered animals for miles around. He did not have a proper piggery but kept the animals in old railway carriages which almost seem to be scattered at random in his muddy old yard. It could be quite dangerous treating any of his sows. Although fat they were roused to anger by sticking a needle into a backside and quick to turn around and attack. Any pig of any size should be treated with caution, and you should always take protection with you when you step into a pig pen. The protection is usually a large board behind which you can shelter while you scamper for the exit. On one occasion I treated one of Les's sows for Erysipelas when it was comatose with a high temperature. It could not have cared less when I injected it with a large dose of penicillin. I returned the next day to check on its progress. Les was not about so I looked into the pen and the sow appeared to be just as I had left it the previous day. Like an idiot I did not take a board into the pen to examine her. Her temperature was normal and as I wacked another dose of antibiotic into her rump she promptly woke up outraged and chased me for my life out of the shed. With my medical bag my only form of protection I stuffed it into her open jaws as she came to get me. She spat it out with contemptuous ease but it did give me enough time to get out and slam the door behind me. That little episode taught me a lesson – never to trust another adult pig again, and certainly not one owned and bred by Les Johnson – late of the Parish of Welney.

Welney used to be the home of champions. As the Wash flooded every winter it was very common during spells of

Vet for Hire

very cold frosty weather for hundreds of people to flock to Welney for some skating. I used to do it myself when my daughters were young. Skating races for money with side betting would be arranged all over the Fens and many young lads from Welney would win as they competed with others from Crowland, Whittlesey and Ely, and even outsiders from London drawn by the prospect of prize money. The last local champion to win a national title was a client of mine, a pig farmer from Upwell called Peter Dorling. He was phenomenal and used to keep fit in the summer months when he was not skating by cycling. I understand he could cycle twenty five miles in an hour and even fifty in two hours which was a fair indication of just how fit he was.

One of the Welney skating champions was Ernie James who was not a farmer. He made his living from the land and river by following the seasons and reaping their harvest. In the winter he, along with Josh Scott, was the last man to use a punt gun on the watery wastes of the Wash to stalk and kill hundreds of ducks with one shot. These were then sent by train to the London markets.

At other times of the year he would trap eels and net plovers which were again destined for the markets in London. He made all his own equipment from the nets to the eel traps. He also patrolled the high banks between the rivers trapping moles for the River Boards. He would skin the moles and preserve their skins, adding to his income when he sold them for fur coats.

I got to know Ernie when he was quite an old man in his eighties when I looked after his Labrador dog. He lived with his wife in a small whitewashed cottage on the bank of the Delph River about three hundred yards from Welney Bridge. A visit to attend to his old dog was always a delight and I could always be persuaded, no matter how busy, to have a cup of tea and a slice of cake made by Mrs James. Ernie would occasionally get out his fiddle and Mrs James would leave the room as she hated the noise. Ernie would play the instrument by tucking it into the crook of his arm instead of under his chin so he could sing as he played in a high flutey voice. It was not great art but it was always great fun.

Around this time during the mid eighties I acquired an old muzzle loading fowling gun from a stockman on the sixteen foot called Bob Jackson who delighted in going to farm sales and buying farming antiques. The gun was very old, the stock full of woodworm and the barrel very thin and rusty. Bob reckoned this gun just didn't fit into his collection and did I want to buy it? I gave him £20 for it which we both considered a bargain. I took it at the first opportunity to let Ernie have a look. He showed me how to clean the barrel with boiling water, load it with a clay pipe full of gunpowder kindly supplied by himself and made wadding from toilet paper which he rammed down the barrel. The old Fenland gunners used hay he said when they couldn't get tissue paper. He wanted to put shot into the barrel as well as he reckoned it was quite safe to fire but I manage to dissuade him. He fitted a percussion cap and fired the weapon into the evening sky. Even without the shot it went off with a terrifying bang and there followed a cascade of burning loo paper and rust sparks from the darkening sky. Emboldened by his example I have ever after fired Betsy every New Year and every Burns night to keep the witches at bay and to remember Ernie.

Josh Scott was the classic poacher turned gamekeeper. For many years he made a living like Ernie James shooting wildfowl in the winter and netting plovers for the London markets. In the summer he was a shepherd looking after hundreds of cattle for various owners. He was a quiet, conscientious man with a very dry sense of humour. The first time I met him he had called to the practice to say that a cow he was looking after was having difficulties calving. He met me at the Suspension Bridge on the far side of the Wash road and together we drove in his old Landrover for what seemed like miles down the New

Vet for Hire

Bedford River banking. Eventually we stopped and he handed me a pair of binoculars. I could see the animal in question in the distance in a large field surrounded by drainage channels. She was on her side and straining. According to Josh she had been in this state all morning and needed help. He was right. The only problem according to Josh was that all the cattle were as 'wild as hawks.' He then said that if we drove through them with the Landrover they would take no notice and this is how he set me up! "Just you sit on the wheel on the bonnet," he said, "And when we get close, slip the lasso over her head."

Needless to say it didn't work quite like that and eventually we had to drag the cow out of one of the drainage dykes before she was delivered of a healthy calf. John and I became good friends after that first episode, but I was always wary of his twinkling eye whenever he asked me to do something out of the ordinary like sitting on the bonnet of a Landrover with a lasso as you are bound to fall off and look very silly in the process.

Josh was friendly with Sir Peter Scott the renowned ornithologist, and when he set up the Wildfowl Trust reserve on the Wash Josh was appointed warden. Instead of making a living shooting wildfowl he was now in charge of their welfare and there could not have been a better man for the job. His famous punt gun was now in retirement but he did show me how to load and fire the 'beast.' Punt guns go off with a tremendous bang, clouds of smoke and have a recoil that knocks the punt to which it is attached a good twenty feet backwards and would easily break a shoulder or collar bone if you were silly enough to put either in harm's way.

There were many others in Welney who made the village special. Norman Clayton (known to me and his wife as Bill) was a retired famer who discovered a solid silver dish and jug from the Roman period when digging out one of his old apple trees in the orchard. It was housed for many years in the

Fenland Characters

Fitzwilliam Museum in Cambridge. He too was very keen on wildfowling and kept a field in the Wash to be able to shoot ducks in the winter season. I used to accompany him for either the morning or evening flight and it was quite magical to listen for the ducks coming in as the sun rose mistily over the Fen, or even better in the evening at sunset and then once it was dark to go for a pint in the Lamb and Flag. When Bill's shooting days were over he gave me one of his two shot guns as a present. He died fairly soon after this and I received a phone call from the police enquiring about Bill's guns. I had registered my gift correctly but they thought I had his other one as well. I told them I did not and was asked whether I might know its whereabouts. I did not know for sure but Bill had told me he had wanted to be buried with his gun by his side as it had been given him by his much loved wife Gwen. I gave them this information and as far as I am aware this was the end of their enquiries.

Arthur Carter was known in the practice as 'Crabbie.' He always sounded very depressed whenever he had to phone for the vet. He kept pigs beside the school at Meadow Farm and, although he looked miserable most of the time, he was in fact quite jovial. When he grinned, exposing his top teeth and gums, it really was a sight to behold. His wife was a great baker and to make a visit at lunchtime was quite a revelation to see how he could pack away large amounts of home made pies and pasties, even as quite an old man. He often looked over the fence into the next door sheep farm owned by Roger Giles to give advice and generally comment in the genial way that he had. Roger tried very hard to farm sheep successfully grazing on the Wash but he lost many sheep which was financially disastrous. It was never very clear the cause of his losses. Many distinguished vets and pathologists did try to find the answer but it was probably a combination of liver fluke disease, which was my theory, and ragwort poisoning.

Roger very sensibly gave up sheep farming eventually and

Vet for Hire

has been for many years now a very successful landscape gardener bringing much needed employment to the village.

Tommy Rolfe was a shepherd on Welney Wash and employed by the many farmers and graziers who rented the fields on the Wash during the summer months to graze their livestock. I was never very sure how he survived financially in the winter but he did have a thoroughbred stallion which he kept at Mr Hall's farm in the middle of the village. Horse breeders would come from Newmarket and Cambridge with their mares to get the services of Tommy's stallion as it was reputed to be from a great line of race horses. The rendezvous was always the car park at the Lamb and Flag where the deed was done as it was a very short trot for the stallion from his stable in the farmyard. I was never happy about how the animal was housed and I kept meaning to take Tommy to task on the matter but he died in tragic circumstances. He fell asleep one night with the coke burning stove emitting carbon monoxide through an open vent and he never woke up. The stallion had gone by the time I became aware that Tommy had died and I never found out what happened to it.

Jack Johnson was not from Welney but owned a farm at Three Holes just down the road. He spent a lot of time in the village as he often had stock on the Wash, but more importantly he had a Percheron stallion called Sam. Sam was a national champion and much in demand to cover mares. Sam's foals were highly esteemed.

Jack would bring Sam to Welney very often to rendezvous with owners with mares outside the Three Tuns which was down by the side of the Delph River. He was excellent to load onto the lorry to bring to the village as the horse knew there would be a mare in season at the other end and to say he was keen was always an understatement. After the deed was done Sam was equally ready to go home. Unfortunately when the mare wasn't in season and Sam did not get what he came for he would not get back onto the lorry! Somebody in the Three Tuns said "give the hoss a pint." Sure enough after the beer was produced and Sam drank it and loved it he loaded without a problem. After that first time Sam always got his pint and would stand outside the pub with his head and shoulders through the door and was allowed to drink the beer from the overflow tray.

Jack was another large man and an excellent farmer. He had a reputation for being irascible and short tempered and the veterinary partner that I succeeded lived in dread of a visit to Lode Hall farm. Almost from the start Jack and I got on well. The only occasion when his temper flared up at me was when I was about an hour later on the farm than the appointed time. He shouted at me and I shouted back that I had been busy on an emergency, which was quite untrue, and he calmed down and all was well. Jack was a very kind man who would often go out of his way to help anyone in distress. My daughters loved going to the farm when they were little as we were always invited into the kitchen where they were filled full of chocolate cake and Ribena.

Jack died young in his early fifties and typically left money for all his friends in the Three Tuns to have a good drink. Sam, his beloved stallion, lived to a ripe old age. In his late teens he developed a cancer in his right testicle which became very swollen and painful. There was discussion at the time whether he should be put down but as he was in good fettle otherwise we decided to go for surgery. The front field at the house was the operating theatre and after the intravenous injection Sam crashed to the ground. The surgery was fairly alarming but in the end straightforward. He woke up easily and quickly afterwards but would not stand up. I was very concerned that I had put him through the procedure only to have to put him down. A heavy horse that won't get on its feet after an operation gets muscle damage and the longer they are on the ground the worse the prognosis. However a colleague went back in the

Vet for Hire

afternoon and injected a stimulant that is normally used only in dogs and Sam leapt to his feet. He lived for three more years after this and was still able to cover and get mares into foal, even with just one testicle. His end came one morning when he became cast in the stable as the result of colic. He was on his side, very distressed and in pain. It was obviously the end and I put him down. I did not have the appropriate drug available or my gun so I had to borrow a twelve bore shot gun. This, when used correctly, is very effective, quick and non messy and Sam was very soon put out of his misery. It was a sad end to a very full and fertile life and he was buried as Jack would have wished in the front paddock where he had had his operation and in which he spent most of his life.

Of course Welney did not have a monopoly on characters and Parson Drove had a few as well. Chief among them was W. H. Crowson, also know as Bill. He kept cattle in the village and reared calves which he bought at Melton Mowbray market. The calves, usually three at a time, were put to foster cows that would suckle them until they were old enough to be weaned onto solid food. It was a good business so long as you bought well and Bill had a good eye for a bargain and a healthy animal. He supplied calves to most of his neighbours who were in the same business, often bringing at least six back at a time from the market which he would sell on at very little profit. He so enjoyed market day that if he went on holiday, usually to Great Yarmouth, he would always travel from there to Melton and then back to Yarmouth. He would have to leave at 4.00am and wouldn't get back till nearly 10.00pm as it was such as long journey with his Landrover and trusty Rice trailer, but Bill always reckoned it was worth it. His son is made from the same mould. Gog, or Mick as he is known, is equally outgoing and generous as his father before him and as a child was once observed dragging a donkey cart along the road with the donkey trotting behind. He explained that he thought the donkey was a 'bit tired' and was giving it a rest.

Sonny Hill and Harry Aldridge had adjoining smallholdings

Fenland Characters

in Coates and along with other farming activities they both kept pigs. They shared an ancient thatched barn which was later dismantled and re-erected on the East of England Show ground. They would take turns at sitting up with their sows when they were farrowing and at the first sign of trouble they would phone for help, even in the middle of the night. They were fairly unlikely characters to make common cause. Sonny always had a wide grin on his face, hence his nickname. Even with a toothache he could not help smiling. Harry was much quieter and a bit dour but they made a good team. On one occasion Sonny called me in the middle of the night to ask for a visit to one of his sows called Lucy in the morning (all his sows were named). When I told him he had woken me up just to ask for a routine visit he was horrified. He thought that the duty vet was waiting in the clinic throughout the night for any emergency calls or to give advice. Needless to say he never did it again unless it was a genuine emergency.

Not all the unique characters were born and bred in the Fens. Many wartime refugees or ex POWs stayed on and many were employed on the farms. Gustav, whose last name I never knew, was one of these. I think he came from the Ukraine and he was employed by Eddie Tribe in the town of March as a pig man and was very good and hard working. The main problem with Gustav was that Mr Tribe's foreman was a very pleasant German called Gerald and Gustav was never going to take orders from a German. As he explained countless times, he had a German bullet in his backside. It led to countless arguments and conflicts.

Gustav made a device to stop sows savaging their piglets. It was like a loose halter around the head but when the animal opened her jaws to bite, a bolt incorporated into the webbing would jab into the back of her neck causing her to desist – or so he said, but I was never that convinced. However I was seldom requested to sedate or anaesthetise any of his farrowing sows that were inclined to infanticide. He eventually left to

Vet for Hire

emigrate to Australia, taking his patent device with him, and Gerald was left in peace to manage the farm as he wanted. He was succeeded in his job as head pig man by Tony who was Italian and got on much better with Gerald so that harmony was restored on Mr Tribe's farm.

Bert Deptford was a farmer of note in the March district when I joined the practice in the late nineteen sixties. He kept show ponies as a hobby which he exhibited with distinction all over England. He bred ponies and sold the surplus for a good price, keeping back the best for himself. As the most junior member of the veterinary team I was not allowed anywhere near them normally, and Alec Noble as the senior (in age and experience) partner looked after them on a day to day basis.

This all changed one Sunday evening when I was on call. I got a message from Bert asking me (as the emergency on call vet) to go and visit a foal with colic. The man himself was there as the stables were at the back of his house. He was looking very concerned and I did not tell him that this was the first case of colic I had attended as a qualified vet. I had seen and treated other cases but only as a student and only in the role of deputy and general onlooker.

Even to my inexperienced eye I could tell the youngster was in a lot of pain. I could not do an internal examination as the foal was much too small to allow a rectal examination. I had to content myself with giving it an intravenous pain relieving, gut muscle relaxing injection. This seemed to do the trick but I was called back about two hours later as the foal was again writhing in pain. I gave it a larger dose of a more powerful injection and hoped it would work, and all the time Bert, although obviously worried, was very supportive and pleasant, even giving me his trademark poke in the tummy as I left and a little wink. Others in his position would have been questioning my credentials and demanding the presence of a partner.

Fenland Characters

When he called me out again one hour later I did ask Geoff Oakley to come along. He was the partner I was going to replace in the practice and I felt I needed some back up. As I suspected the foal had a twisted gut I took the precaution of taking the gun with me as I thought we might need it and did not want to take such a big decision on my own. This was after all my first case of colic.

Geoff and I examined the poor little beast and it was obviously in agony. Bert looked on quietly without making much comment.

I whispered conspiratorially to Geoff, "I think its got a twisted gut and its going to die."

He nodded his assent and reached for the gun to put it out of pain when it crashed to the ground and died. Bert did not say much but seemed more concerned about me as I was visibly upset at the turn of events.

A post mortem was done in the morning and confirmed that the animal had indeed got a twisted gut and nothing and nobody could have saved him. Bert could not have known that when his prize foal died but at no point did he voice his concern or doubt about the treatment it was having when he could so easily have made my first colic case, which was bad enough with the patient dying, even worse.

Not all my clients have been as pleasant and generous as those I have talked about. Farmers can be notorious for being slow payers and some can be pretty mean. One I knew was so tight fisted that it was said that he had perfected the art of pealing an orange one handed in his pocket so that he wouldn't have to share the bits.

What you will get from most Fen folk, farmers or not, is straight talking. They tell it as it is.

Vet for Hire

I stopped the car one day to ask directions to a house and knocked on a door as there was no one about. I was answered by an old man who must have been at least ninety.

He peered and squinted at me and said, "I know you, don't I?"

"Do you?" I replied. "I'm Russell Lyon, the vet."

"That's right," he replied with a grin." You're getting on a bit now, aren't you?"

I was at least thirty years his junior but that meant nothing to the old boy.

Chapter Six
Pampered Pets

We all think our pets are special, and they are. For some people they are as special and as precious as children. They can be pampered and cosseted in a way that a child growing up would rebel against, but the average dog or cat will find no fault with an owner who overindulges them. Having a pet as a child substitute is fine to a degree providing it does not cause any health or behavioural problems, but it so often does.

The first obvious sign of a pampered pet is its weight. Labradors are so often overweight it is not unusual for clients to bring a dog into a clinic thinking it is underweight in comparrison. Instead you are mostly confronted by a young, healthy dog, full of life and fit. Persuading an owner that they have a good, healthy dog can often be as difficult as telling them that their favourite pooch or cat is vastly overweight, and this is a skill that all vets need to acquire. It's even harder if the owner is also morbidly obese, which is so often the case. Get it wrong and you will lose a client, and the patient sure as heck won't lose weight. In fact it's as likely to put more on. The constant refrain is "but we hardly feed it anything at all" which usually conveniently ignores all the titbits that are fed almost ad lib by more indulgent members of the household, anything that falls from the toddler's compliant hands and the fact that the dog is also pinching the cat's food.

Cats cunningly often have more that one feeding station in various houses. Most clinics now operate a 'weight watchers' club for chubby cats and obese dogs with some success. Obesity can, as in people, cause a multitude of health problems.

Vet for Hire

You could be forgiven for thinking that the problem of overweight animals is confined to household pets but that is not the case at all. Equine practices are very used to dealing with overweight ponies. Shetland ponies have a Thelwell image and can thrive on very little. They were bred to work and live off just a few blades of grass and a wisp of hay but most are now kept as ornaments or children's pets and can easily get very fat, and either develop fatty livers and die or get laminitis. Donkeys unfortunately can be just as much at risk. The other kind of pony which is overindulged is the show pony that is pampered, petted and overfed. Most owners and judges of show classes want to see a pony in 'show condition' which is a euphemism for overweight.

One of my clients did not believe that her wonderful show pony, which had won lots of rosettes in the local shows, was in fact overweight and was lame because it was too heavy and had laminitis. I could not convince her otherwise, and as she did not believe me and wanted a diagnosis that would fit her way of thinking I referred her pony to the Animal Health Trust for a second opinion. The report duly came back that I was right. The pony was overweight and had laminitis and the client had a large bill to pay. I was very pleased to go through the report with her and she went away with her own copy to underline the message.

***

Laminitis is a very painful condition of the feet in horses and ponies. It is very similar to having a bang on a finger or toe nail and there is bleeding. It hurts a lot. The nail turns blue-black because of the blood and eventually comes away. Imagine the pain involved for the animal when all the feet are affected with laminitis and it still has to stand and walk. There are apparently up to 10,000 new cases of laminitis every year and probably double that with long term chronic effects of the disease. It is most common in the spring and is caused by the animal having too much lush green grass to eat, something which, when left to their own devices throughout the day, they will do without any encouragement. After all, it's what they evolved to do over millions of years. They are herd animals designed to spend at least sixty percent of their time eating. This is fine if they are on poor grass, grazing wide open plains and getting lots of exercise. Most are not and are kept in grassy paddocks which are positively hazardous, especially in the spring months.

The lamina is the soft tissue in the foot which connects the pedal bone (the last bone in the foot) to the rest of the hoof. It is a highly vascular and sensitive structure and the term laminitis just means inflammation of these tissues. Laminitis happens when the blood supply to the foot becomes interrupted, mostly because of overeating. Arterial blood is shunted directly into the veins without going through the sensitive lamina with often disastrous results. Within a short period of time permanent damage can be done to the foot due to the lack of oxygenated blood. If the disruption is severe the attachment between the pedal bone and the horny hoof will fail. This sometimes means the pedal bone will descend through the sole of the foot and the pony ('no foot, no horse') has to be put down as the pain cannot be relieved and there is no realistic hope of it living a normal, equine life. I have fortunately seen only a few with extreme laminitis as most can, with correct treatment and surgical shoeing, have a reasonable pain free lifestyle. The pony I bought for my children for a nominal sum of money had acute laminitis at the time of purchase as he had been left and ignored in a large field full of grass that would have fattened twenty bullocks, never mind one pony. I put him in a starvation paddock where he could wander at will and had very small regular amounts of feed. He recovered well, became a firm family favourite and was able to be ridden and enjoyed life well into his thirties.

***

Vet for Hire

Pampered pets can have many different behavioural problems. These can be as simple as fear of thunder and other loud noises, to peeing and pooing indoors, and most difficult of all, aggression against other animals or even the owner. Most of these difficulties can be helped by an understanding vet who has time to explain and devise techniques for dealing with the very many different situations which arise or an animal behaviourist (who can be a practice nurse) who is often very helpful. A pampered dog is often prone to separation anxiety and this can be very difficult to deal with. A dog that becomes so dependant on its owner that it will howl, bark and destroy the happy home if it is left on its own for even a short period of time is very trying for an owner, and the situation is very distressing for the dog too. Fears and phobias are very real but a well meaning owner may make a phobia worse by giving the animal lots of attention and affection when trying to calm it down. This can make the fear even worse the next time the animal is left alone. Treating any type of fear can be a long and involved process. Drugs may help initially but the long term solution lies in an effective retraining and conditioning programme which takes time and lot of patience. Most people suspect there are far fewer phobic animals when there is more than one animal in a household, which may be true. However, I have had over the years a succession of dogs that seemed to teach each other a fear of thunder. Saffron, my rescued Golden Retriever, had a separation anxiety which was cured almost overnight by having a companion Border terrier called Tuppy. However, she also had a fear of thunder which she seemed to pass on to her hairy little friend. She in turn taught the next pet in line, an otherwise sensible if slightly dotty English setter/ Labrador called Tula Tika, that thunder and loud bangs were a signal that the Gods were displeased with her and were going to strike her down any minute.

I found the only thing that helped Tula overcome her fears was valium tablets. One 5mg tablet took away the worst of her symptoms and she stopped shivering and wanting to climb on my knee. With two tablets she would lie quietly under the table and go to sleep, and with three, as I did once give her, she seemed to want to go out and watch the lightning!

Some scared cats and dogs can be helped by a chemical which is naturally produced by animals. These are pheromones. The substance can now be produced and synthesized artificially and can be delivered either by a spray or a plug into a wall socket diffuser. The canine product is *Dog Appeasing Pheromone* (DAP) and helps to reassure dogs their environment is safe and secure. A similar product for cats is *Feliway.*. These chemicals can be very good in the early stages of anxiety and may reduce the need for a companion animal to offset the problem but will be no use when the cat or dog is in a state of panic.

There is a relatively new product on the market called *Zylkene* designed to calm an anxious pet. It is not a sedative and can be bought over the counter without the need for a prescription. It is derived from casein, a product found in milk. Researchers had noted that when a baby suckles – human or animal – there seems to be a calming feel-good factor not associated directly with the actual feeding process and with not feeling hungry any more. This was isolated by a drug company and marketed under their trade name. I was very sceptical initially but it does seem to help to calm and alleviate the stress that some animals do feel, even with minor changes to their lifestyle.

Separation anxiety is not confined to dogs. Many highly strung horses, usually of the thoroughbred type, can be equally afflicted. I used to look after an equestrian centre where many horses came to compete in show jumping competitions. It was not unusual for an animal to arrive with a stable companion such as a Shetland pony or even a goat. One horse arrived for a weekend's activities and the owner forgot to bring the goat. The horse was a very large Hanoverian type who travelled in style in a fine horse box but would not settle in the stables and kicked down a separating breeze block wall. It had to be

Vet for Hire

calmed with a sedative which of course meant it could not compete so the weekend was a complete waste of time, and all because the owner forgot to bring Gertie the goat. Horses are herd animals and most of the time they need company of their own kind (or similar!) and it is cruel to keep them lonely and isolated in a field or stable. Drug treatment is not the answer even though it might give a short term fix. I had read somewhere that *Prozac* had been helpful in reducing the neurosis of a stallion which, of necessity, had to be kept fairly isolated from others of its kind. I mentioned this to a client who had a friend with a similar problem with her horse and she prevailed on her vet to give it a try. The dose of *Prozac* for a horse was quite high, and as the treatment was not licensed it was rather expensive. Unfortunately it did not work, costing the owner around £800 to learn that drug treatment is not always the answer for a behavioural problem. It might help in the short term but the long term answer for animal fears lies with desensitising programmes, training and counter conditioning which takes time and patience but ultimately can be very rewarding.

***

For a few years it was very fashionable to keep Vietnamese Pot Bellied pigs as household pets. They are intelligent creatures which can usually be toilet trained and will go for walks. At the height of the craze in the USA magazines were devoted to them and the unfortunate animals were dressed in all sorts of stupid clothing. Pigs have always been kept close to people as a good source of protein and were fed mostly on human food waste products and scraps. This feeding of table food waste has now been banned as it can be a vehicle for infecting the animals with Foot and Mouth disease.

Pigs as pets are very bright and will take over if given the opportunity. I had a client who until fairly recently had a Pot Bellied pig which he had had from a very young age. He kept her indoors and made a great fuss of her, even picking her up and cuddling her until she became too fat to lift. When she was about three years old she suddenly got the upper hand and turned against him and would bite and chase him whenever the opportunity arose. He had to don cricket pads and brandish a long brush to defend himself whenever he went into her quarters to feed her or clean out the paddock. Matters came to a head one day after a particularly vicious attack. He was so frightened of her he phoned and asked me to put her down. Fortunately I managed instead to find a new home for her and she now lives happily in a grass field with a hut for shelter and another Vietnamese reject for company.

Not all pigs end up biting the hand that feeds them. I knew an old chap in March in the Fens who would regularly take his Large White sow for a walk that almost always ended up at the pub. It was never on the lead and trotted behind him like any well trained dog. The man, pig and pub have long since ceased to exist and I never did find out what the other regular customers thought of their porcine drinking mate. It could not happen now. Pigs can be taken for walks but only if the route has been checked and approved by DEFRA in case the porker's countryside ramble endangers other commercial pig units by potentially spreading disease.

***

When I went to live and work in the Far East I knew that most of the time I would be working with dogs and cats. I had not realised that there seemed to be two classes of dogs in Hong Kong. The 'haves' – the pampered pets – and the 'have nots' – usually strays.

The strays, often called village dogs, lived in packs around the villages and barbeque sites in the New Territories. Some did have owners and were used as guard dogs but almost all were unregistered, which means they had no microchip and

Vet for Hire

no rabies vaccination. These village dogs seem to do quite well and on the whole don't look undernourished. They are, however, absolute pests to walkers, especially those with their own pets on a leash, as the strays have little fear of humans and will bite and chase any intruders on 'their patch.'

The urban strays have a much tougher time than those in the villages. Many tend to congregate around building sites where they are encouraged to live during the construction phase, being used as unofficial and free security guards. They are penned up and fed during the day but at night they are allowed out within the perimeter of the security fence, keeping out all potential thieves and intruders. This is all unofficial, of course, and when the building is completed the developers will either call in the Ministry of Agriculture officials who will round up the dogs and kill them, or more likely just let them out to perpetuate the stray problem elsewhere. This happened when the Disney Park was being built on Lantua Island in the north west part of Hong Kong and a public outcry shamed Disney into paying for the strays to be collected, vaccinated and neutered, and where possible rehomed. Some construction workers will nurture small black dogs, feeding them up then killing and eating them, especially during the winter months which according to many in the Far East are the best time of the year. The eating of dog is supposed to confer strength, stamina and virility and the methods used to kill them are especially cruel. I was reliably told they were either drowned, or even worse hung up and beaten to death. This is apparently done to tenderise the meat and is typical of the casual and disgusting cruelty which is still prevalent in the Far East. It is illegal in Hong Kong, but it still happens.

Such practices are not illegal on Mainland China where animals are skinned alive for their fur, and bears are imprisoned for years in small cages where they are unable to move, and have their bile taken through a dirty cannula inserted into the gall bladder by owners with no formal medical training. Once their bile giving days are over the bears are killed for their fur and paws. It was reported by a mainland paper that one such animal escaped from its cage, killed the owner and was last seen heading for the hills. It was never recaptured. Hurrah for the bear, I say!

Not much pampering for the animals in China then, but I am told that traditional attitudes are changing, and for many of the wealthier classes in China pets are now seen as a new and much valued status symbol.

During the winter months in Hong Kong the daytime temperature hovers around 15°C and hardly ever gets below 10°C and I became quite accustomed to peeling coats off little dogs before being able to examine them. I recall one day when the daytime temperature hovered around 18°C when I had to peel off three coats before I eventually got to the dog. I asked the owner, "Why so many jackets on your little dog?" and I got a sheepish grin and was told, "Because he is very cold."

In Hong Kong many young couples have a small pedigree dog which can be a child substitue as well as a 'must have' item, and it is often very spoiled.

Feng Shui literally means 'wind and water.' We in the West call it geomancy which means the art (or science, as some prefer) of manipulating or judging the environment to produce good fortune. In Hong Kong if you want to build a new house or apartment block or find a suitable site for a grave you must first of all call in a Feng Shui expert.

I sort of knew about Feng Shui before I left the UK but I failed to realise that Feng Shui also applies to pets and many doting owners. Needless to say the better off parts of Hong Kong society will go to absolutely any expense to indulge their much beloved pampered pets.

Designer home dogs and cats have their own luxuries too.

Vet for Hire

Burberry make feeding bowls in their distinctive plaid design and Gucci has put its name to a pet carrying bag. All are said to have excellent Feng Shui. Designer fakes are easily found in Hong Kong on any street market but for a pampered pet's owner it has to be the real thing. Fake designer goods will not do for their darlings, quite apart from being bad Feng Shui. Fakes for the owners are OK but never for their best friend.

Online shopping sites offer Feng Shui toys for sale and lush newborn cradles are available in pink or blue. For older pets beds come in a variety of styles including a timber sleigh, and for dogs with bad backs there are orthopaedic designs too. From the vet's point of view these must be especially useless.

There are upholstered pet sofas in a choice of fabric including leather and these are available in chaise longue form. Owners can also buy special toilets for their pampered pet pooches and these can be buried in the ground for hygienic disposal of biological waste, which sounds like a very good idea but is not much use if you live, as most people do, in a high-rise skyscraper.

Some companies that cater for cats will customise a scratch post in the same material as the living room carpet – as if the animal cares about colour coordination! Laser cut steel was the latest trend for stainless steel wall mounted feeding bowls. Pet doors come in hi-tech designs too, with a full range of fully automatic electronic models for standard or patio doors which I could not believe would catch on with skyscraper living, but I did hear of a client in Scotland who lives in a high-rise tenement block having just such a device on her front door which her cat uses on a regular basis. Presumably it doesn't mind climbing the stairs.

However, there are very few new ideas left in this world. When I was visiting a centuries old Chinese walled village I noticed what looked suspiciously like a dog/cat flap in the outer wall. My enquiries proved that the hole in the wall was just for that purpose; to allow the dogs to go outside to perform when the fortified gates were shut for the night.

***

One Hong Kong couple with more money than sense were very worried about their dog falling out of the window thirty floors up. It is not an uncommon occurrence apparently, although unsurprisingly we tended not to see the victims afterwards. They called in a designer to help, as closing the window was not an option. It would have been a lot cheaper, but was still not an option. A designer called Cheung devised a sliding Japanese style shoji paper screen fitted to a sliding track over the window just slightly smaller than the animal's body – and all for a minor $2500 (about £200). The same designer (well he would, wouldn't he?) came up with the idea for the dog to share a bed area without actually being in the owners' bed. A smaller bed was created with a stepped platform next to the owners' bed to which it was attached – all custom made for only $1500. The bed, in case you thought the price was excessive, included a storage area below for toys and a refrigerator for the animal's food.

The same animal had a combination grooming and toilet area in the bathroom. The family had a cat too which meant that an acrylic screen was placed over the cooker to stop any possibility of the cat getting burned. The family also got the designer to create a false ceiling and an elevated walkway for $20000 to allow the cat to climb about and explore to reduce its boredom level.

Off course not all pets are so fortunate. A story in the South China Post told the sad tale of Dou Dou the Shih Tzu whose owner had not been paying enough attention to Feng Shui when she chose a grooming parlour for her beloved pet. The dog was taken to the local poodle parlour for a shampoo and

Vet for Hire

came out having had a body shave instead. The owner, a Miss Bonnie Lou Yee-Lin was incandescent with rage as the dog, according to Miss Bonnie, was so upset he could not bring himself to look in the mirror. This apparently was a regular source of pleasure to Dou Dou prior to the clipping.

"He looks like a Chihuahua with a skin rash," she said. "I couldn't recognise him until he wagged his tail and kissed me. Even the upward sprouting hair above his nose that gave him his chrysanthemum face has gone."

The owner complained to the Consumer Council but they said that Miss Bonnie had to prove that the grooming that had gone wrong had resulted in significant unnecessary suffering to the dog or his owner. Compensation would depend on whether Dou Dou had refused to eat, had become ill or was suffering a temporary depression, and whether the owner could prove it or not. Trying her best to do just that Miss Bonnie Lou Yee-Lin said, according to the newspaper:

"He is very self-conscious. He loves the mirror and the camera. He used to eat right in front of the mirror but now he just looks away from it... I have never seen him naked. I don't know if he has any birthmarks. How can I identify him?"

She had obviously conveniently forgotten that Dou Dou had been micro-chipped and there was no possibility that he could not be positively identified. However, she had the parlour owner rattled as he apologised many times for the error. "What more can I say?" he said. "We made a mistake. What can I do really? Do you want me to reattach the dog's hair?"

Meanwhile Miss Bonnie – who said she was reserving her legal position at the moment until she consulted her solicitor – found a way to cheer up her fretting pet in the six months for the hair to grow back:
"I am buying him more attractive and colourful outfits to

make him feel better – we have to cheer him up and let him know he is handsome."

Hmm – only in Hong Kong? Well actually I'm not so sure. We in the UK pride ourselves on being animal lovers, but over the top pampering can often cause unintended harm wherever you live.

***

Dogs can and often do bite the hand that feeds them. I had the misfortune to look after a poodle owned by a Fen farmer and his Chinese wife. The dog was called Pepe and it had a very poor opinion of people and any vets who wanted to give him vaccinations or any other treatments. He was allowed to sleep in the marital bed between the couple. If either couple turned over during the night in a way that disturbed the dog he would bite. The wife thought this was a bit of a giggle but I could tell her spouse was understandably not too keen on the arrangement. I think the farmer was trying to make me feel better as I tried unsuccessfully to vaccinate the beast and had to insist they brought him into the clinic where we could get him away from the female owner and put on a muzzle. In the surgery he was much easier to deal with as he knew he wasn't in charge and was much more submissive. He was an object lesson in what can happen when an animal is allowed by pampering to dominate a family. If the dog is small it is at worst a nuisance and a social inconvenience but if it happens with a large breed such as a Mastiff, German Shepherd, Rottweiler or similar then it can have tragic consequences, especially when young children are at risk. Such large animals when out of control can be positively lethal.

Chapter Seven
Eat to Live

Most animals, whether they are farm or domestic animals such as dogs will, if they are healthy, eat with gusto whenever they get the opportunity. It's a relic from the wild: eat as much as you can when it is available as it may not last and your next meal may be a long time coming. This behaviour is still seen very commonly in rescued dogs that, as strays, have often had to struggle to feed themselves.

It is often thought and said that most animals have an innate sense of what is poisonous and what is safe to eat. It's not true. What is true is that horses, goats and sheep are selective feeders and will seldom eat poisonous plants, but they might, if circumstances caused an animal to abandon its inbred caution, chew and swallow something toxic.

Like sheep, goats are notorious for dying mysteriously with nothing but some frothy phlegm on their lips to mark their passing. The transition from seemingly good health to death is often very short and sudden too and such was the case at a smallholding in Somersham where an owner had found, to her consternation, three of her six goats very suddenly very dead, yet the others were still lively and in good health. While on route to such a catastrophe it is all too human to try to run through all the possible causes of sudden death in goats. High among these are clostridia infections which can cause sudden death. I thought it unlikely in this case as we sold the owner clostridia vaccine and knew she was careful about storing it and using it correctly twice a year on all her animals. Another possibility for sudden death is Anthrax and I knew certain fields around Somersham had been implicated in the past with killing sows with the infection. As a student one of my practice mentors used to make a habit of quizzing me while on the way to calls as to possible diagnoses given certain sets of circumstances. He would then say that, of course, you should never pre-judge what you are going to see as it is all too possible to make symptoms fit a preconsidered diagnosis and miss something altogether more obvious.

When I arrived at the smallholding there were three dead goats in the small paddock. The others in a small field adjoining were all fine and still happily browsing grass, hay and willow leaves. True to form all the dead animals had flecks of foam at both the nostrils and lips. My attention was drawn to a small bonfire in the centre of the field. Most of the material was burned but around the fringes of the fire, which was now extinguished, was some brown and green vegetation. As I poked around it was pretty obvious what had been burned. A tree that had been overhanging the property – a yew – had been cut back and the branches burned, but not completely. I did not need a post mortem to know the cause of death. Yew is deadly poisonous to most animals and even a mouthful is enough to kill any cattle, horse, sheep or goat stupid enough to try eating its evergreen foliage. Taxus baccata contains an alkaloid taxine which is a very powerful cardiac depressant. There have been reports of animals with symptoms of collapse before dying, but all the cases I have seen have been dead. There is no treatment and death occurs very rapidly after ingestion. I was amazed to read a report in a recent Veterinary Record that Soay sheep may be resistant to the poison but it's not a theory I ever would be prepared to test. I did read somewhere that people have committed suicide by powdering dry yew needles and then mixing the deadly poison with water before swallowing the mixture. In this case with the goats I think their natural curiosity was stimulated by the burning bonfire with the fatal outcome. I did a very rapid autopsy on one of the animals just to be sure that my suspicions were not unfounded and discovered, as I

Vet for Hire

expected, bits of yew clippings in the animal's stomach. Over the centuries many church yards have had yew trees planted around the tomb stones. This may have been for supernatural reasons – to deter witches or the Devil – but there is a much more likely and practical reason. Where yews are growing then farmers, knowing the risks, are much more likely to make stringent efforts to stop their grazing animals from getting into a churchyard and being poisoned. It was a way of stopping sacred ground from being desecrated by livestock.

Taxine, the poisonous ingredient in yew, has long been regarded with interest by the medical profession and pharmaceutical companies as a possible treatment for all manner of life threatening diseases such as cancer, and it would not be without precedent if this did happen. Foxglove, for instance, give us digitalis for treating heart disease but is wisely avoided due to its known toxicity. The same may yet be true for the yew tree.

Yellow is the colour of spring. Daffodils are swiftly followed by buttercups and dandelions. Then we have fields of oil seed rape which delight the eye and raise the spirits just as much as the lengthening days and shorter nights – so long as you are not allergic to rape seed pollen. A much more sinister plant which flowers after oil seed rape is ragwort. The flower is a slightly darker shade of yellow and at first sight the adult plant can look quite attractive as it is often to be seen in otherwise poor looking pastures or on railway sidings. Don't be fooled. It is deadly to horses. The plant is seldom seen in well managed farms but can proliferate around hedgerows and in fields where horses graze.

No self-respecting horse or pony will eat ragwort when it is in full flower. It is too bitter. However, many animals have been tempted to nibble away when there is no grass growing in a paddock and the only bit of greenery emerging through the soil is the ragwort. It is then at its most poisonous. It might also be eaten when grass is cut for hay and ragwort plants are mixed in with the cuttings. It is then quite edible, but still lethal. It has long been supposed that sheep and cattle are more resistant to the poison. My father, a livestock farmer, used to say that the best way to get rid of ragwort was to allow sheep to graze in the field as the plant was emerging and the sheep would eat the stem and destroy the plant without harming themselves. This was before chemical sprays were available. While I am sure that sheep are much more resistant to the poison, it is a procedure I would not recommend.

The problem with the plant, *Senecio jacobea*, is that it contains pyrrolizidine alkaloids which can cause terrible liver damage. The plant is usually eaten over a period of time and often this protracted exposure results in slow developing liver damage. Unfortunately, when the symptoms do finally appear in horses they are acute and horrendous. The damaged liver becomes very small and fibrosed and the affected animal develops an acute encephalopathy. The symptoms often arise very quickly. Quite suddenly the animals become blind, totally unaware of their surroundings and wander aimlessly and often in circles. Sometimes they can be aggressive when anybody tries to restrain them to stop then harming themselves. Others stand pressing their head against a wall as if they have an almighty headache.

These acute signs can occur very rapidly. I recall one evening being called out to an amiable riding pony which had suddenly 'gone mad,' according to the owner. It had blundered through a barbed wire fence and onto a railway line. When I arrived a train was expected at any moment and no one had thought to ring the station as a warning. We managed to get the animal off the line but it could not be restrained from crashing through a post and rail fence. The poor beast was in a terrible state. It was bleeding from various cuts and wounds and it was still walking blindly in a circle with a rope attached to a head collar and looked appalling. It had lost a lot of weight and

Vet for Hire

was sweating profusely. You could see all its ribs as if it had been starved for weeks and when I managed, with extreme difficulty, to look into its eyes it was very jaundiced. There could only be one conclusion and one outcome. I rushed back to the car to get the injection to put the poor beast out of its misery just as quickly as possible.

Occasionally there are milder symptoms before the brain is affected which can often be diagnosed by blood testing, for example after a horse has been noted to be in poor condition or by observing an animal in its surroundings. It is amazing despite all the warnings how many horse owners still allow horses and ponies to graze in ragwort infested fields. But it is also difficult to detect the plant in hay as it can look like dried thistles. The responsibility is really on the person making the hay to ensure there is no ragwort dried and mixed in with the grass.

Treating the patient for liver damage with multivitamins and other liver supporting medicines can be successful if in the early stages as the liver can, if not too damaged, repair itself. However, once the brain is affected there can only be one outcome.

Eradicating the plant can be difficult. Pulling it out and burning before it seeds can be very hard work, but very effective. Anybody doing this would be well advised to wear gloves as the toxin can be absorbed through the skin. Chemical herbicides can work very well if used at the correct time and dilution, but they are expensive, although it must be cheaper and better than a dead horse.

Cows are almost by definition pretty stupid animals and some of the poisoning cases I have encountered involving them could probably be seen as their own silly fault. They are inquisitive and seem to want to lick and chew or sample any unusual objects that might happen to be within reach.

Eat to Live

Lead poisoning used to be very common, especially in calves. The usual scenario involved calves confined within a pen whose sides were held together with old ladders or redundant wooden pieces of farm carts or gates. Fen farmers like to make use of every bit of material lying around to make do and mend and hardly ever throw anything out. Very many of these old structures were painted with lead paint and seemed to have an irresistible attraction to young calves with often fatal consequences. They will froth at the mouth and grind their teeth, often a symptom of acute abdominal pain, and stagger around the pen bumping into anything that gets in the way as they are blinded by the poison. When the cause of the poisoning was pointed out to the stockman the common riposte was that the pens had been like that for years without causing a problem, which was often the case, but once one animal starts to lick, the others join in with an often terminal outcome. A drug called sodium calcium edentate given intravenously in saline can reverse the milder symptoms and many can recover if you get to them in time.

Farms are dangerous places for livestock. They are never very tidy and adult cattle are often poisoned by lead leaching out of old batteries or sump oil that has been carelessly discarded. Like calves they cannot resist the urge to investigate with their tongues. But it could also be argued that they, as a species, cannot be blamed for the farmer's faults, who certainly should know better.

One of the strangest cases of poisoning affecting adult cattle occurred on a river bank near Wisbech. The banking had been grazed bare of vegetation by many cattle. It was grossly overstocked and the farmer, aware that the animals had virtually nothing to eat, brought in loads of onions which he dumped in strategic piles along the bank. In the past I had seen cattle being fed onions when they were confined in yards and this did not cause a problem, apart from horrendous halitosis, as they had other things to eat as well as onions.

Vet for Hire

Catherine Mair was the vet on call the weekend when the problem arose and she had been requested to attend the cattle on the bank, as one was dead and quite a few others were very lethargic and drowsy. She asked me to come along just to help out.

The very concerned farmer met us and we drove down the bank to where the dead animal lay. As the vehicle came to a halt beside the dead cow another beast in a weakened state passed very red coloured urine as it stood munching disconsolately beside a pile of gently rotting and stinking onions.

The dead animal was very anaemic. The blood was like thin beetroot juice and this was confirmed in others by checking a few of the damaged survivors who were just standing around as interested onlookers the way cows usually do. The spectators were too weak to walk away and were easily caught. The cause of the pallor was obviously – the onions which were being consumed in large quantities by the cattle as they had nothing else to eat. Onions fed to cattle will cause a haemolytic anaemia where the red blood cells are damaged and destroyed, and the give away symptom is red coloured urine caused by the haemoglobinurea.

The farmer had been pleased that he had been able to feed his animals virtually for free with the onions but it had cost the life of one of them. The others made a good recovery with vitamin and iron injections and a swift removal of all the onions and their replacement with good quality fodder. It was an expensive lesson for the farmer, who had no idea just how dangerous onions could be for livestock with nothing better to eat.

Pigs are like human beings – omnivorous – which means they can and will eat almost anything, given the opportunity. When they are kept indoors they have a limited scope for poisoning themselves but it can happen. Outdoor pigs can be just as much at risk from their environment as grazing animals. Pigs kept in orchards, as many smallholders do, will fill themselves to excess given the opportunity with any windblown apples, pears or plums, with a similar outcome to ourselves. It's very uncomfortable but it rarely kills.

I occasionally diagnose salt poisoning in pigs kept indoors. It can be seen in any age of animal. Affected pigs will fall onto their sides and paddle their legs furiously as if they are running. Unlike pigs with other central nervous symptoms caused by meningitis they do not squeal in distress while they are fitting. They are silent. It can be difficult in younger animals to confirm the cause of the illness as it can look very similar to streptococcal meningitis or an E coli infection resulting in bowel and brain oedema, but these animals will squeal in distress unlike those with salt poisoning. It's not a hard and fast rule but a reasonable guideline.

However, diagnosis does involve some detective work. The real cause of the syndrome is really not salt poisoning, although there is excess salt in the brain. The overload of salt in the grey matter is due to water deprivation.

In the winter months the lack of drinking water is usually caused by frozen pipes. After a spell of cold weather inadequately lagged pipes can become frozen solid and farmers who are not alert to the problem will find that some pigs that have not been able to drink enough will be off their feed, depressed and constipated. If action is not taken immediately animals will start dying. When pigs are put into new groups, particularly at weaning, they may not understand how to operate new nipple drinkers and this can be another cause of convulsions due to salt poisoning. These pigs may have to be shown how the drinkers work or sometimes they may be too small to even reach the water source. Very occasionally pigs will be deprived of water by larger pigs when there are not enough drinkers to go around and smaller animals are too

Vet for Hire

scared to compete for a drink.

Fortunately, although recovery in severely affected animals can take twenty four to thirty six hours, the treatment is cheap and effective. By using a watering can or even a hose pipe, sick pigs are allowed to drink small amounts of water regularly. Water is trickled into the side of the mouth even when the animal is lying on its side. Care has to be taken when an animal is having convulsions to prevent water getting onto the lungs as this could cause inhalation pneumonia. Affected pigs have to be kept quiet, undisturbed and in the dark for at least twenty four hours, but the majority will recover. Most pig farmers, once they have had this type of poisoning with their pigs, learn very quickly never to let it happen again. A pen full of pigs flat out on their sides and fitting is very scary. Even if all the pigs recover it's a scene most farmers will never want to see repeated.

The most common reason for dogs visiting a veterinary clinic even today is food poisoning. Dogs can be incorrigible scavengers and cannot resist devouring anything rotten and smelly. The obvious outcome is acute vomiting and diarrhoea but fortunately even without treatment the animal will usually recover spontaneously but never learns the lesson of what not to eat.

When I was a young lad growing up on the farm one of my first jobs was feeding the hens and collecting the eggs in the 'Old Mill' which housed a few hundred of the feathered creatures in a deep litter system. I was always accompanied by Ruski, my little Border terrier dog. She was a useful companion as inevitably, where there are straw and feed and hens there are rats, and Ruski was a rat killer par excellence. She was deadly. However, she could not hope to catch them all and dishes of rat poison – *Warfarin* – was placed at strategic points throughout the building. The rats ate the poison and would die, or if in a depleted state Ruski would get them and finish them off. She would always have a little lick of the rat bait. and I was concerned enough to check whether this could do her any harm and was told that warfarin was not harmful to dogs. Indeed Ruski never seemed to come to any harm. It was only later when I became a vet student that I realised just how wrong that advice was. As a final year student I was visiting my sister's farm and she asked me to check her beagle bitch called Trudy. She was very quiet and cold and pale. I really didn't understand what was going on and advised her to take the dog into the practice where I was working. I was half way home when the penny dropped for me that Trudy had probably been poisoned by *Warfarin* and I told Grace to rush the dog in as quickly as possible. My diagnosis was right and Trudy received the antidote, Vitamin K, in the nick of time and lived to tell the tale.

Warfarin acts as a poison by stopping blood from clotting so that the affected animal bleeds to death internally. The anti-clotting mechanism of the drug has been used for many years with human stroke and heart attack victims and has been very successful in prolonging life. It has also been used in horses to treat Navicular disease as it allows blood to travel more easily through the horse's foot which aids the healing process.

Over the years rats have developed immunity to *Warfarin* and stronger and more potent types of the drug have been developed. This is all good but it does mean that dogs that have eaten rat bait are far more difficult to treat. In the past one or two injections of Vitamin K was all that was required to bring about a cure but now animals may need blood transfusions and Vitamin K treatment for up to two weeks after an accidental poisoning that is often fatal.

It's a sign of the times we live in that rat poison is not now the most common form of poisoning in dogs – it's actually chocolate. Most owners know that chocolate intended for human consumption is dangerous to dogs because of the

Vet for Hire

theobromine content of the confection, but still it happens all the time and mostly due to the carelessness of the owner. Christmas time is always the peak period for chocolate poisoning. Dogs will steal from a Christmas tree and anything lying on the floor or on a low coffee table is fair game. One year we had the same dog poisoned three times in a week. Despite all that was said on the first and second occasion the owner, through total neglect, forgot each time the animal went home to put the sweets out of reach. "But I only turned my back for a minute," was the excuse. The dog survived each time but it may have sustained lasting harm.

Dark chocolate is the worst culprit and causes vomiting, diarrhoea, collapse and death through heart failure. There is no antidote. You can only treat the symptoms. If you get to the animal quickly enough before the chocolate is digested then making it vomit is a good option. Otherwise it has to be hospitalised and put on an intravenous drip.

Some owners will buy chocolate intended for pets from pet shops that does not have theobromine in it but for the life of me I cannot understand why they do this. Chocolate of any description for pets is fattening and bad for the teeth. A pet, if you must give it a treat, is just as happy with a chunk of raw carrot.

There are other foodstuffs around the average house which are toxic to dogs of which most people are unaware. Grapes, raisins and sultanas have all been shown to be poisonous to dogs, although no one seems very sure what it is in the fruit that is dangerous. It is suspected that a possible fungal toxin, pesticide or environmental toxin may be to blame, but no one is really sure and it does beg the question of what the risks may be for humans?

Cats are fastidious creatures and they, unlike dogs, are unlikely to eat anything horrible that will give them food poisoning. It used to be quite common, however, to find cats poisoned by a mouse bait poison called *Alphachloralose*. The cat would catch and eat a mouse that had been poisoned, and in this way ingest the poison for themselves. The symptoms are quite alarming. The cat initially goes through an excited phase quickly followed by aggression and then convulsions. Despite the fitting they develop hypothermia which is the key to diagnosing the condition. After you have seen a few cats poisoned by this drug it can be quite easy to make the diagnosis. The treatment is even easier. All you need to do is put the cat under a heat lamp and turn them over from time to time to ensure that fluid does not accumulate on the dependent side of the chest. After a few hours the cat will waken up, the poison metabolised out of their system, and they seem to be none the worse for the experience.

I have not seen this type of toxicity for quite a few years now and I presume that alphachloralose is no longer being used so extensively as a mouse killer.

What does appear to be on the increase is poisoning due to ethylene glycol better known as antifreeze. Both dogs and cat will drink antifreeze as it is very sweet and they like the taste. It causes depression, coma and death to most cats. There is a form of treatment in dogs which is not effective in cats. The antifreeze causes severe kidney failure and as there is no possibility of dialysis or renal transplant for cats, the outcome is invariably fatal. It has been used by malicious and dangerous people with vendettas against dogs and cats to kill them in a horrible way.

Kidney failure can also be caused in cats by lily pollen. The flowers, when part of a floral display or in a bouquet, look magnificent and each has on their stamens a brown pollen which gets everywhere and is difficult to remove from clothing. It has recently been discovered that this pollen, if it gets onto a cat's coat and is licked off as cats will do,

Vet for Hire

causes severe renal failure. I treated a young cat just a few weeks ago with terminal renal failure and thought for a time that the cause was either congenital or drinking antifreeze. It was eventually realised that lily pollen was to blame. The knowledge came too late to save that little cat and it died after days of intravenous drips and renal medications. At least with the owner now aware, no more lilies will be bought and that home will be just that bit safer for any other cats.

It is very common for an owner to suspect that a neighbour has poisoned their pet. Most of the time it is not the case, but just occasionally it is true. When I was working in Hong Kong there was a spate of poisonings. Weeks could go past without a dog dying but then the phantom poisoner would strike again and there might be two dead in a week. In all the cases an undiluted pesticide had been injected into meat and the dog would die within minutes. As far as I know, despite police investigations no one was caught. Still in Hong Kong a more fortunate animal was rushed into the clinic one morning in Sai Kung. It was a cross bred sixteen week old German Shepherd puppy. The owner had a gym and the dog was taken to work and put in a pen close to a footpath. An elderly man walked past every morning and the dog would bark, causing the man to shout at the pup and poke it with a stick which made it bark all the more and he would then try to kick it. This went on for a few days, then one morning the old man gave the dog a piece of meat as he went past. Within two to three minutes it had collapsed, foaming at the mouth and having convulsions. On inspection of the pup I suspected it was a form of organophosphorus poison. I injected atropine which is the antidote for this and put the dog on a drip. Fortunately I was right and the puppy survived to go home later in the day. The old man who felt he had nothing to apologise for was visited by the police, prosecuted and fined. The dog never went back to the gym again and was fortunate to survive. Had treatment been delayed by even minutes it would have died, becoming another statistic in man's inhumanity to animals.

Chapter Eight
Foreign Bodies

Most pet owners will be aware that there are times when their animal may pick up and swallow objects that could not remotely be construed as food, not even by the most stupid dog on the planet. These objects will vary from sticks and stones and rubber balls (probably the most commonly swallowed item), to some very bizarre items indeed.

It is relatively simple to diagnose when a dog has swallowed a foreign body – some of the time. Labradors, but there are many other breeds equally culpable, will pick up, carry and chew sticks, and will sometimes eat them. There may be no intention on the dog's part to eat the wood. It may not actually want to swallow it ot it may not even get as far as the stomach, but will instead get lodged across the roof of the mouth, jammed up against the hard palate and kept that way by the upper sets of molars. The owners are not always aware what is going on and will present a dog which has been frantically pawing at its mouth or dribbling and unable to eat. It will often look a bit cross-eyed as well but this is not a diagnostic feature, more a personal observation from seeing very many self-inflicted dogs.

Bob, a German Shepherd crossed with a Labrador, springs readily to mind. I was called out to Welney – yes that place again – by Bob's owner who was worried that the dog was not eating. I would not usually rush to examine Bob's mouth without some form of sedation first as he was a big dog and not averse to having a bite at any vet who might want to take liberties with his body. In this case I knew just by looking at him that I had to look in his mouth and quickly. He was

Vet for Hire

dribbling, shaking and panting. He actually looked like a rabid dog. His owner and I backed him into a corner and when he was held firmly by his master I grabbed his jaw with my fingers pressed over his jowls, which covered his fangs. It's a small measure you can take to reduce the risk of your fingers being bitten when you prise open a reluctant mouth. Sure enough my instinct was right and there was a piece of kindling he had been chewing wedged firmly across the roof of his mouth. I rushed back to the car and found the longest pair of artery forceps in the bag. With his jaws wide open again it only took a moment to extract the obstruction and Bob was 'cured' of his mystery ailment. Strange to relate, as it doesn't often happen, Bob from then on seemed to trust me and let me examine him and even give him his vaccinations without his usual protests.

Most foreign objects do, however, find their way without impediment into the stomach, and then into the intestine where they will obstruct the bowel so that the animal cannot keep anything down. It will vomit even water and quickly becomes dehydrated and very ill.

My eldest daughter's dog is a Labrador that I found and bought for the family as a puppy. Rascal goes on the beach most days as the family live by the seaside. All her life she has been addicted to digging out and swallowing stones. She will even put her head under water with her eyes open in order to select suitable material. For ten years at least I have been warning Carol of the dire consequences for the animal if a stone becomes lodged, but to date the dog has always managed to vomit up stones after the walk and there never has been a problem.

Unfortunately the same cannot be said for the majority of objects swallowed by animals. Whenever a vomiting dog is presented in any veterinary clinic, especially if they are young animals, most vets will automatically consider an ingested and obstructing foreign body as the possible cause. If you are very lucky and the dog will allow you, it is sometimes possible to palpate a foreign object in the gut by feeling through the abdominal wall. Most of the time, however, an X-ray will be required to make the diagnosis. If the object is radio opaque (ie. you can see it!) then the diagnosis is simple. The surgery, providing the intestine is not badly damaged and necrotic, is usually straightforward. If, as sometimes happens, the diagnosis and treatment has been delayed for any reason then parts of the bowel may have become necrotic. If this has happened then the damaged intestine has to be removed entirely until healthy tissue is reached and the healthy ends rejoined. This is called an end to end anastomosis. This operation is technically more difficult and there are increased risks of peritonitis but most patients usually make a good recovery.

On many occasions the obstructing material is something other than a stone or similar, in which case the diagnosis can be much more difficult. Plastic, rubber or fabric cannot usually be seen on an X-ray.

Some years ago there was a problem in a small village near Wisbech. Items of ladies' underwear were regularly being stolen off washing lines. I solved the case one Saturday night when a large yellow cross bred dog was brought in as an emergency. He had been vomiting for two days. Blood tests were not helpful, apart from showing some dehydration, so I sedated him and took some X-rays. There were no obvious radio opaque foreign objects in his gut, but the intestines were much dilated with gas and fluid. I decided, after consultation with his owner, to do an exploratory laparotomy (ex lap) as I was fairly convinced something was blocking the bowel. I was right. His small intestine, which was very long, was blocked by a pair of ladies tights. The material was 'concertinaing' his gut and I had to spend a considerable portion of the evening removing the tights in bits from three different holes. The surgery was uneventful if a bit time consuming, and at the end of the evening the dog was looking much better as he had

Vet for Hire

been on an intravenous drip during the operation which had remedied the dehydration. I went to bed quite pleased with my efforts but come the morning I was less happy with myself, as overnight he had vomited some ladies knickers from his stomach which I had completely missed. When I presented the lingerie to the lady owner she confirmed that they did not belong to her – the wrong size she said, and the mystery of the knicker knicker was thus solved.

The story does not end there. The dog's owner had to tell the police as they had become involved, and go around her neighbours confessing her pet's misdemeanours. The dog was called Will (short for Wilful, so well named!) and his operation did not stop his activities. On two other occasions, despite being alerted to Will's little perversions, he managed to swallow more lingerie, although on both occasions we managed to retrieve the underwear by making him vomit them up from his stomach before they found their way into the gut and did more harm to his intestinal tract.

Will and his family eventually moved away from the area and I have no knowledge of his eventual fate, but I do suspect he may have come to a sticky end.

I have removed many different items from dogs' intestinal tracts and you might think ladies underwear would be fairly high up in the list of unusual objects, but not so. One of the most bizarre was a pornographic plastic Mickey Mouse. The animal had been vomiting for some time but we could see nothing on X-ray. The intestines were not dilated but it came to a point when something had to be done and I did the usual ex lap. On opening the abdomen I could feel an object in the stomach. I fixed the foreign body in the stomach with my left hand so that it did not move and made an incision through the stomach wall. Mickey's head popped out. He looked in pristine condition with all his colours intact and was winking in a suggestive manner. As his body emerged from the viscera his wink was explained by his hands and Walt Disney would not have wanted to be associated with his behaviour. I gave the toy back to his owner (not the dog!) in a plain brown bag without comment. I didn't trust myself!

While on the same sort of subject I must tell you about the Siamese cat. Cats seldom swallow foreign objects as they are usually much more fastidious than dogs about what they eat. This one did though, and strangely he was quite an old cat that should have known a lot better. Mostly it's younger dogs and cats that do silly things. This animal presented all the usual symptoms but nothing too obvious showed up on X-ray so I elected for surgery. I removed a used condom from his small intestine caught by the knot in the rubber at the ilio-caecal junction. Goodness knows why the cat had swallowed it. The owner said it was a balloon but he knew and I knew and he knew I knew it was a condom. The cat made a good recovery.

The most hair raising object ever removed from a dog's stomach to my mind must be a very large kitchen knife which I saw on X-ray for the first time. The owner, a butcher, had been feeding the animal small cubes of meat from the point of the knife when the dog, in its greedy haste to get more and more, jumped forward quickly and swallowed the meat and the knife in one go. The X-ray was spectacular. The blade was in the stomach but as far as could be seen had not penetrated the stomach wall. Fortunately the removal of the knife was just a matter of anaesthetising the animal and grasping the handle which could just about be visualised at the back of the throat with the mouth opened wide. It was a straight pull out in the manner of a sword swallower and not a drop of blood was spilled. Amazingly enough the dog was none the worse for his knife swallowing antics but I'm sure the owner will never again try feeding his dog from the point of a knife.

Sometimes an exploratory operation carried out for the right clinical reasons yields nothing which can be very frustrating.

Vet for Hire

Mostly when looking in an abdomen for a foreign object they are fairly easily found. When nothing can be discovered I have invariably spent a long time, as I am sure have many of my colleagues, searching in vain through a gut to find no abnormalities, and certainly no strange objects. Strangely enough on many of these occasions where the presenting feature has been vomiting but nothing has been found the animal wakens up and stops being sick. We always tend to say jokingly that the animal got better because we let the bad air or the demons (!) out, or something else to that effect, but it is amazing how often it happens after an operation for good clinical reasons to try and find the cause of vomiting that nothing is found and the patient gets better anyway.

In the summer months foreign bodies are very commonly found in dogs. These are not swallowed but find their own way in without any assistance from the animal into the feet, ears, eyes and up noses. These are the common places but they can be found anywhere in the body. Grass seeds or wild barley awns are the common culprits but it can be anything from long blades of grass to slender pieces of wood.

It's almost like someone above flicks a switch. It goes from not having seen a case all year to suddenly, and usually towards the end of June, getting as many as two or three affected animals, mostly dogs, in a day. No animal that goes snuffling through the undergrowth is exempt, but hairy dogs are much more likely to suffer from the incursions of grass seeds. It goes on right through harvest time and the season usually finishes sometime in October.

The removal of grass seeds is sometimes easy but at other times can be fraught with difficulty. Those in the ears can sometimes be removed if the dog is very cooperative and quiet. Using an otoscope to see the object and inserting the long and thin crocodile forceps through the otoscope you can grasp the seed and pull it out if you, the dog and the owner are very lucky. If not the patient has to be sedated at the very least and sometimes needs a general anaesthetic to be able to remove the seed or seeds as it hurts. Grass seeds in feet can be even harder to find. The patient almost always has to be sedated as the discharging sinus has to be opened up surgically and the penetrating tract followed until the object is found. Of course sometimes it is not found as it can literally be anywhere in the leg. One dog of my acquaintance had a grass seed penetrate its foot and eventually not one but four were removed from its neck region. One dog had a seed in its foot and it could not be found. I thought it must have fallen out but I put a poultice on the foot overnight just to be sure. I was rewarded when I took the bandage off the next day to find the culprit in the dressing. Some might not be found for years. Alex Dallas who owns the London Road Veterinary Clinic did a rather complex operation on a dog's ear which had been giving trouble for a long time. The operation was a bulla osteotomy, which means cutting into the inner bony ear behind the ear drum to allow an infection to drain, and found five grass seeds that had probably been in place there for years. How they got there is an even bigger mystery.

I make a point of telling clients in the grass seed season to inspect their dogs' feet and ears when they come home from a walk as it is very common to find these pests sitting in the long hair just waiting for their chance to penetrate and cause trouble. It's so easy to do and could save the dog a lot of pain and the owner a large bill.

You might think that foreign objects in bodies are going to be much more the province of small animal vets and pets rather than farm livestock but you would be wrong. Cows and cattle are well known for ingesting things they ought not to. That curse of the late twentieth century – the plastic bag – is very likely to be swallowed by ravenous bovines. And if it's not bags then it's plastic string, be it blue or red, which has not been removed from the hay or straw before being presented

Vet for Hire

to the feeding animals. Cows are often not that choosy about what they are eating. Plastic bags are a blot on the landscape as they do not rot down or disintegrate. However, I have seen evidence that the acids in a cow's rumen will at least partially digest plastic. A cow that has swallowed some plastic may have a bit of indigestion for a few days but a lot of the time a farmer will not know unless he or she sees it swallowed.

Cows are also prone to swallowing nails or bits of wire that get into the forage. They do not do this voluntarily, it's just that they don't see what they are eating. It is most unlikely to happen with a goat, sheep or horse as they are all very selective and dainty about what they eat. A bovine uses its prehensile tongue to curve around food material and eat it in great swathes. It has very little control about what might be in the centre of the pile of grass, hay or silage that it is about to consume.

Bits of metal in a cow's stomach can cause a big problem. Initially the animal will go off its food and will show a lot of abdominal pain. They have a characteristic grunt which they emit if the vet pushes a diagnostic fist into the lower abdomen. It's a risky procedure quite liable to get you kicked, and cows can be particularly adept with their hind feet if provoked in this way. Kicking is a bovine specialty and hurts badly!

The indigestion can only get worse if, as happens occasionally, the metal object has a sharp point which penetrates the stomach wall and then proceeds into the chest where it impales the heart and eventually kills the cow.

The practice in which I was nurtured as a young and aspiring vet had among its veterinary equipment a World War 2 mine detector. This was a fairly obsolete bit of kit but was useful at detecting metal in cows' rumens. Clinically you could be fairly convinced that metal of some description was in the abdomen but no one really wanted to proceed to the next bit of treatment – the rumenotomy – unless the metal detector had done its stuff and predicted a successful outcome. Care had to be taken not to produce a false positive when the instrument was applied to the animal's midriff as in most cow byres there are plenty of extraneous bits of iron in the stall that would give a false reading.

Having been convinced by the metal detector and all the other clinical signs that there is a piece of ironmongery where it should not be, the next stage is an operation to find and remove the wire or nail. Cows are fairly tolerant creatures and will allow the vet to search around in their stomachs, providing you first give them lots of local anaesthetic to stop any sensation. Providing you do this they will stand quietly while you cut into their left side, locate the rumen which is not difficult to do as it is huge, and plunge your hand and arm into the thick green porridge which is the stomach contents. The search takes you right down to the bottom of the stomach and those vets who are not very tall may have to stand on a block to be able to reach right down to the target area as a metal object is always right down at the lowest point of the abdomen. If you are right you will find the object, extract it triumphantly and show off your trophy. The cow and the owner will be happy and you will have justified your fee. If you can't find anything then the operation still has to be paid for, which makes life more difficult to explain to the farmer who likes to see results for his money.

I have been told, and it may be just one of these apocryphal tales that certain vets in the 'old days' would relate, that if they could find nothing they were quite ready to have a sharp bit of wire or a nail to hand (so to speak!) which they would produce at the right moment and pretend they had found in the abdominal contents. It made the farmer more ready to pay the bill.

I'm sure it's not a technique that is practiced these days!

Chapter Nine
How Cruel Can You Be?

When a newly qualified vet is admitted to the Royal College of Veterinary Surgeons, he or she has to make the following declaration. When I graduated it was called taking the oath. The main part of it is as follows:

"I promise that my constant endeavour will be to ensure the welfare of the animals committed to my care."

On the face of it that is very straightforward and no right thinking person, let alone vet, would or could have any problems in upholding that promise.

There have, however, been times during my life as a farm animal vet when that promise has been tested, not so much by clear issues of bad husbandry or cruelty which are comparatively easily identified and dealt with, but instead by the many grey areas of farm practice which have made me feel very uncomfortable. When I qualified in the sixties there were many farming practices which at that time were seen to be quite acceptable. My own father, along with many of his like minded neighbours, would take calves no more than two to three days old to market in the boot of the car. These youngsters were dairy bull calves that were surplus to requirements. The unfortunate calf was put into a hessian sack with only its head protruding and was auctioned off to the highest bidder. As a result many young animals died after a few days from an infection easily acquired from other young animals because their immune system could not protect them. My dad was not a cruel man. In fact he was the very opposite, but he saw nothing wrong in a practice that was widespread and acknowledged as perfectly acceptable. The only concern at the time by most farmers engaging in the practice was whether the frightened animal, and most must have been terrified, would have diarrhoea into and through the sack with the resultant smell and mess. No thought was given at all about the effect, both physical and mental, on a very young creature. Now anyone doing this would rightly be open to prosecution by the RSPCA.

Calves and lambs were castrated without anaesthetic (and still are legally in some circumstances). Disbudding and dehorning was also commonly practiced without first giving a local anaesthetic. Father, to his credit, would not allow this on the farm as he saw how much better and easier it was to do the job by using local anaesthetic first, but I knew many including close relatives who did not. The cruelty at that time (in the fifties and sixties) was mostly casual and unthinking. Fortunately, with time farming practices have improved considerably. In the nineteen eighties the Government of the day produced Codes of Welfare for all farm animals which did a great deal to improve husbandry systems which promote good health and take into account the behavioural needs of farm livestock. But I had to point out to clients on a number of occasions that these Codes of Welfare were minimum standards to which everybody in the livestock industry had to comply. Really good farmers would want to have even higher standards.

Even today the vast majority of eggs are produced by hens in battery cages. It is possible to buy eggs from hens that are kept more humanely in deep litter systems or outdoors where the hens have freedom to move around, but the eggs produced in this way are inevitably more expensive. Hens in battery cages have a short and miserable existence. They are unable to express their most basic needs to stretch out, scratch the earth and nest as they would if given the opportunity. And yet if you go into a building full of battery hens in cages you would be struck by the noise of hens talking and squawking as

Vet for Hire

they interact with their neighbours without a seeming care in the world. Farmers who still keep hens in this way use this in defence of a system that, at the time of writing this book is still legal. They argue that the animals are kept in a temperature controlled environment with an ever ready source of clean water and food. What can be wrong with that, they would say?

A society, The British Hen Welfare Trust, now exists for rescuing battery hens when they are about to be dispatched to the slaughter house to be made into chicken curries after they have passed their peak of egg production. These fortunate few are given the chance of a different lifestyle and most grab it with gusto for within hours they are enjoying living a happy free range life. I used to be involved with a feed company who offered a post mortem service to farmers who bought poultry food from them. Hens that had died would be brought to the surgery, often at the weekend, for a diagnosis based on the pathological examination. One Saturday afternoon I was faced by a pile of dead hens, two very close to death and one other. As I worked my way through what I had to do and euthanased the two almost dead animals I reached for the last hen and she promptly looked me in the eye and laid an egg. It was against all the rules but I could not kill her. Instead I put her under my jacket and took her home. She was installed in the stable with the pony and given the unimaginative name of Henrietta. Within a day this poor, bedraggled creature who was missing about fifty percent of her feathers had found the garden. She was actively making herself a dust bath in one of the flower borders and was doing her best to look for worms, despite having had the top part of her beak removed, debeaking being the common measure taken to prevent cannibalism in the battery cages. It was amazing considering all she had known before was a battery cage. Within a few short weeks her feathers grew back, she looked magnificent with a fine red comb and produced an egg every day. The children usually had to go looking for them as she rarely laid her egg in the same place twice. She made friends and enemies whereever she went and she had a very free range. One neighbour had to take special measures to keep her out of his vegetable patch and another fed her jammy toast when she called in the morning at his French windows and pecked on the glass until she was fed. She lived for another two and a half years from the time of that post mortem session. She ruled the yard. The dogs gave her no problems and she would groom the cats with her twisted beak, looking for anything edible. I don't think she was unique in any way. Most other battery hens I am sure given the opportunity would have behaved in much the same manner and her life with me and my family showed me just how wrong it is to confine a sentient creature in a cage for all its short life.

Most modern methods of husbandry which have evolved during my time in large animal practice have (for the most part) improved the standards of animal care. There are now good guidelines for stockmen and women relating to most aspects of keeping farm animals which have eradicated many bad practices, but many do still exist. And it is still quite legal to keep hens cramped together in battery cages.

Growing up on a dairy farm as I did meant looking after cows in byres (cow sheds) that were tethered by neck chains in individual stalls for all of the winter months. They were well looked after but never moved from their stalls unless they were ill or produced a calf, and then they might just spend a few days in a loose box. Their calves would be removed at birth so that mother and offspring had no chance to form any sort of bond. In the spring when the grass had grown sufficiently they were allowed out into the fields. The sight of mature, matronly cows throwing their heels in the air and cavorting around in delight like young calves was sufficient to show me just how awful it must be to be restricted for months at a time. It must almost have been like a hostage handcuffed to a radiator, although the cows would not have been afraid for their lives. Now this practice is very outdated and cows

Vet for Hire

are mostly housed in barns without being tethered and can move around at will. This is much more humane, although individual cows can be bullied. They will also walk into the milking parlour at least twice a day to be milked. Cows like a routine and need exercise, and it seems a vast improvement to the way we kept our cows when I was but a lad.

Sows are still kept in farrowing crates while they are giving birth and for up to two weeks after for feeding their piglets, which is justifiable as it does reduce the incidence of youngsters being laid on by clumsy mothers. When she is about to give birth the sow wants to make a nest as she would in the wild. One of the saddest things to observe is a mother in a farrowing crate where she can only move forward and backward a few inches and has a rubber mat to lie on but no straw. I have seen many frantically try to get bedding material from the rubber and rub their nose raw in the attempt. Keeping them without straw or paper bedding is perfectly legal. When I tried to get a certain farmer to give his sows at least a handful or two of straw to make them less stressed he refused as he said it would clog up the drains. Pigs reared and fattened on slats would also be much happier with some bedding material. It is again quite within the rules not to use any but the animals would be much happier and less likely to have behavioural problems such as tail biting caused by overcrowding, which is not allowed, and boredom, which unfortunately is! Dry sows, those that are pregnant and not feeding piglets, used to be kept like dairy cows in stalls for up to three months at a time to which they were tethered by means of a belt around the chest that connected to a chain. This chain was attached to a metal ring imbedded in the concrete stand on which they lay. It was a cheap and easy way to keep sows but has now fortunately been banned throughout Europe because of the welfare implications, but I have been assured that many of our EU partners turn a blind eye to the rules and pig farmers continue to flout the law. It is worth remembering that it results in the widely available, cheaper bacon on the supermarket shelves which undercuts our own produced to higher welfare standards.

Farm vets are under pressure in some cases where a grey area exists. Where exactly to draw the line? The Codes of Welfare are very useful in this respect but cannot cover every contingency. It may be as simple as a farmer or farm worker being too heavy handed with a stick when moving stock. Vets who are too forceful in their opinions may alienate and lose a client and anyone who seeks to alter a method of husbandry that he or she thinks is harmful by friendly persuasion may find their advice is ignored.

Small animal vets have to deal with different types of pressure from clients, but the underlying cause may be the same – financial. Very few people will be deliberately cruel. Cat or dog owners may not be able to afford an essential operation or treatment and yet they will not sanction euthanasia. They would rather keep a much loved pet in pain than relieve its suffering with a humane but deadly injection.

It is very common to examine an old dog or cat in the consulting room for a vaccination or some other minor procedure, only to find the poor creature has a mouth full of rotting teeth with a smell to match. Some clients will not hear of the animal having a dental problem, although it is strongly pointed out just how awful it must be for the patient. The owners fear that their pet will not survive the anaesthetic due to their advanced age. However, many of these are not done because of the underlying reason – the cost. Some owners are genuine in their ignorance and truly do not realise the pain and distrss that their pet is suffering. It is evident on recovery from the proceedure just how much they have been affected as there is an immediate change in the animal's behaviour and demeanour. Suddenly the dog or cat feels so much better that it can appear to be two or three years younger.

Owners with a pet that is suffering from an incurable disease

Vet for Hire

may find it very difficult to 'let go' to allow the animal to die with dignity and relieve its suffering by euthanasia. It can be a problem for the vet to press the case for 'putting to sleep' as the individual vet may feel that it is a reflection on them that they cannot cure the disease or mitigate the pain short of euthanasia. In many of these cases putting the animal down is the best possible outcome when all other avenues have been explored. Cost may come into the equation and an owner may feel guilty that they cannot afford the ideal treatment and have to opt for euthanasia for a condition that could be treatable. It can be equally hard for the vet looking after the animal as well as the owner.

Whatever the reason it can be very sad to lose a much loved pet, and in many cases it is like losing a member of the family. But very often I am very relieved that the animal's suffering is at an end.

One of my most memorable cases was an old Siamese cat that had lived in Japan. As far as I could make out he had been treated for some time while in the Far East for chronic renal failure. His kidneys could not cope and he suffered from dehydration which was apparently treated once or twice a week with painful, subcutaneous injections of saline. When he reached our verterinary practice in the UK he was immediately hospitalised for evaluation and treatment. He remained in hospital for two or three days and, while on a drip, improved and even managed to eat something. But as soon as he went home his condition worsened and he was back to square one almost overnight. Each time he came back in it proved more difficult to help him with a drip and it was eventually decided it was cruel to keep him alive. Unfortunately the lady owner would not hear of it and had hysterics when the subject was mentioned and the husband was abroad and difficult to contact.

Matters came to a head one morning when the animal, even while on a drip, was in a coma and unlikely to survive for more than another few hours. The lady eventually agreed to euthanasia when I told her rather brutally how cruel it was to make him suffer in this way. She agreed but wanted to take him home to see her husband. The deal was made to let him go home still connected up to the drip and I would follow on behind her car and do the deed in her house.

I found my way into the large country house where the weeping owner was cuddling her poorly, comatose cat in front of the computer screen. Her husband was an American GI in Afghanistan and he was online on Skype talking to the cat and saying goodbye. He was in tears, she was desperately upset and two children were howling in another room, but I was relieved that the cat would not be suffering any more. I slipped the lethal blue injection into the drip line while he was being held by her and was pleased it was all over. I did think it would have been much kinder if the owner had been more sensible and the animal had not been forced to travel and perhaps should have ended his days in the Far East. It was another case where the emotional needs of the owners took precedence over the physical needs of the animal and it was just cruel to prolong his suffering.

The last time I was in Hong Kong doing a locum a little geriatric Japanese Spitz called Sui Pak came through the clinic door wearing red coloured sunglasses. They looked like goggles and I immediately thought of a kamikaze pilot. The reason for the sunglasses was very obvious when they were removed. His left eye was horribly ulcerated as a result of a large wart on the upper eyelid which was rubbing on the eye. He had had it for months and had been given antibiotic eye drops to keep the infection at bay as the owner would not allow surgery to remove the wart. Her pet was a seventeen year old dog with a grade 3-4 heart murmur. But it was well compensated. There was no fluid in the chest. He was not coughing and he was coping well. His few remaining teeth were dreadful, suppurating and stinking. To complete the

Vet for Hire

picture he had a pronounced bacterial infection of the skin around the base of the tail and very full anal glands. Despite all this he was amazingly bright, ate well and was very happy to be in the clinic exhaling obnoxious fumes indiscriminately from just about every available orifice. The owners heard I was back in town and decided I was going to have the privilege of treating their beloved pet. I was known (affectionately, I think) as the 'Abba Issan' which in Chinese means the old doctor. Any reputation I had was based solely on age which the Chinese tend to revere and an ability to smile benignly at all clients – even the most difficult – as I had no idea most of the time just what they were talking about.

The eye ought really to have been removed but in the end I settled for removal of the wart, cauterising the ulcer and a dental to sort out his mouth. The owners agreed to these procedures and the operations were fixed for the following morning. They did not turn up. No dog and certainly no owners. One of the girls phoned the home to find out what was happening and was told they were still too scared to allow the poor dog to have the anaesthetic. I suspect they only came to see me in the hope I could suggest some non-surgical treatment. I left Hong Kong six weeks later and Sui Pak was still sporting his sunglasses. In the UK I hope I would have been able by some means to exert enough pressure on the client to be able to relieve the dog his suffering, but it was not possible and was yet another example of human selfishness preventing an animal getting the treatment he so badly needed.

I suppose I could have reported the case to the SPCA which has a big presence in the former colony but I doubt whether anything would have been done and I would have breeched the fundamental rule of client confidentiality.

In the UK I have, over many years, been involved in helping the RSPCA in prosecuting cruelty cases. None involved any of my clients as I would have been seen as biased in any court proceedings. One of the worst involved pigs that were being kept in overcrowded and filthy pens. The animals were in almost permanent darkness unless the door was opened. Over thirty animals were seized by the RSPCA on my authority as in my opinion all the animals were being caused unnecessary suffering. It was not difficult to come to that conclusion. There were three or four dead animals which had been partially eaten, and most of the others were grossly emaciated. There was very little evidence of them being fed and none of the pens had water. It was an amazingly filthy job catching each pig and the RSPCA inspectors were covered in pig muck and stinking before we were finished. I stayed comparatively clean as I had to examine each animal as it was retrieved from the pen. At least that was my excuse. The animals were taken to a place of safety, a smallholding about twenty miles away and housed in a large pen with lots of clean bedding, food and water. I should think they all thought they had died and gone to piggy heaven. When he was found the owner was prosecuted and found guilty. I was in court when he was sent to prison for three months and banned for life from keeping animals. He was astonished to be found guilty and sent down as he truly thought he had done nothing wrong.

Another case that stands out involved a couple of two year old colts that were found one very cold wet March day in a field in Northamptonshire. Neighbours had reported concerns about the animals and an RSPCA inspector was called to investigate. He needed a vet from out of the area as he was sure that he would have to take the animals into care. He knew the identity of the owners but did not want to involve a local veterinary practice in case they might not be able to give evidence in court.

Both animals were extremely emaciated due to severe diarrhoea. The diarrhoea was like water and both horses were pot bellied and very dehydrated. They also had matted hair over their entire bodies as a result of a condition known as rain

Vet for Hire

scald. There was plenty of feed and water in the field which was well sheltered. They should have been fine but the diarrhoea was caused by immature worms called cyathostomes which had been ingested the previous year. This scouring could have been prevented if the animals had been dewormed with the correct preparation the previous November and again in mid February. Typically, as it was with these young horses, the onset of the diarrhoea is usually sudden and acute due to the immature worms suddenly 'wakening up' from their dormant state in the lining of the bowel. It was believed that the owners had not visited the horses for a few days and had missed the onset of the symptoms.

It was decided to get the animals to a place of safety where they could be looked after but one collapsed when it was being loaded. It was so weak it died in transit and the other colt, despite intensive treatment, had to be put down after two days as its condition got worse and it too collapsed and could not stand.

The owners pleaded guilty to neglect with extenuating circumstances and were fined a lot of money. They convinced the judge not to ban them from keeping animals as they owned many other horses which had subsequently been examined and were all found to be in good condition and well kept. It would have been a huge problem for the RSPCA to have seized them all and the organisation contented itself with regular visits to make sure no other horses would suffer due to neglect.

I only once sat on the other side of the fence and supported the defence of a client accused of neglecting her dogs. She bred Shelties for a hobby and had only a few animals. There had been an outbreak of diarrhoea in her kennels and two or three dogs had loose motions but nothing that alarmed her or required – she said – veterinary intervention. One dog had escaped from the kennel run and had been found next to a neighbour's yard. By this time and due to its escapade it was weak and a bit dehydrated and the RSPCA was called. The inspector decided, after taking independent veterinary advice, that a case could be brought against my client and a date was set for court.

She phoned me in some distress on receiving the summons and after some consideration and looking into the facts of the case I decided to help her. If she was to be found guilty on the charge as put she could have been banned from keeping dogs for life which would have been devastating for her. After reviewing all the circumstances I persuaded her to plead guilty to a lesser charge. She was very reluctant to do this as she did not feel she had a case to answer but the fact was that one of her dogs had escaped from her premises, and had it not been found it could have died.

She was fined for neglect and warned as to her future conduct. For years after she had a regular visit from the RSPCA to check that all was well. She never did forgive me for persuading her to plead guilty and although she paid the court fine as she was obliged, my fee for professional advice and appearing in court to support her was never paid. What happened to the dog? He was fine after a few days treatment.

Chapter Ten
Midnight Medicine

It was very dark and the rainwater was trickling down the back of my neck as I dashed across the muddy, uneven yard for the comfort and security of my car. I got in and then cursed as at that moment I realised I had forgotten to check the batch numbers of the drugs I had injected into the cow I had just treated. I had to get out again into the cold and rain to root around in the boot of the car to find the bottle and record the data in my little red book ready for the computer in the morning.

As I drove home I thought how much simpler and easier life was when I first graduated. No thoughts then in pre-BSE (bovine spongiform encephalopathy) days of the need to trace beef from the plate back to the farm of origin. Come to that there was very little thought then given to drug withdrawal times. Now an animal must not be slaughtered for human consumption if it has been treated for any reason until the withdrawal time of the drug in the beast has been closely monitored and obeyed. Professor Swan was the man behind the Swan report into antibiotic drug resistance in man and animals which first raised public awareness of the risks to consumers from the drugs used to treat animals. A few years before he was commissioned by the Government of the day he was lecturing to first year vet students in Edinburgh. I know because I was there!

There is no doubt that modern medicines convey great benefits to both man and animals and I would hate to go back to the dark ages of medicine and surgery where superstition and elements of black magic took precedence over knowledge and common sense.

Midnight Medicine

The strangest case of midnight medicine I have ever come across was quite recently while I was researching for my book *The Secret Society of Horsemen*. I had done a lot of background work to uncover many myths and rituals which I thought had been lost for all time when I was in The Lamb and Flag in Welney one night talking to a man who knew a lot of the old country ways. I bought him a pint and out tumbled many of the stories and mysteries that had taken me months of research to unearth.

In the Norfolk, Suffolk and Cambridgeshire countryside there were, over the ages, lots of superstitions, customs and beliefs relating to the working of horses. Many have persisted down through the ages, and often with good reason. One of the strangest which my informant was able to tell me about was one of the most bizarre and possibly oldest rituals of all. It was all related to a frog or a toad's bones.

The ceremony, which took place in extreme secrecy, was known in Norfolk and other parts of East Anglia as the 'Waters of the Moon.' The men who took part were all horsemen and were called Toad men or Moon men. The horsemen and ploughmen were believed to be members of a secret society and many believed that the Devil was invoked during the ritual. The men who took part in the ceremony did it to command total obedience in their horses.

Roger described the custom of taking a toad (preferably a natter jack or walking toad) or a frog if a toad could not be found. It was killed and the body put onto a white or blackthorn bush for twenty four hours for the carcass to dry out. It was then buried in an anthill or sometimes a dung heap for at least a month or from one full moon until the next. When the toad was removed only the skeleton remained. This was kept carefully and then taken to a stream of running water at midnight when the moon was full. It was believed that the horseman had to go alone and immerse the skeleton in the current. It had to be

Vet for Hire

watched very carefully as a small bone would detach itself from the rest of the skeleton and float upstream against the current. This was the magic bone – the one to be kept and the one they wanted! It resembled the shape of the frog in the horse's foot and was supposed to have magic powers. I even found a suggestion in my research not mentioned by Roger that this bone was a substitute for something more horrible – a finger from a dead child's hand. While the bone was separating from the rest of the skeleton many strange noises would be heard. Sometimes it was said to be like a gale blowing through trees or a building falling down or even a noise like a traction engine. It was vital that the horseman did not take his eyes off the bone as if he did the power would leave the bone and it would not work. It was believed that the noises were the Devil's work at midnight. It was far more likely that other members of the secret society had followed the lone horseman to ensure their newest member observed the proper ritual and were out there creating all the sound effects. I'm sure the weird noises were also much enhanced by the hallucinogenic effect of staring at an object by moonlight and being next to running water for a length of time. I'm surprised many of the initiates didn't fall in and get a good soaking.

The magic bone was said to be forked like a wishbone from a chicken and was probably one of the pelvic bones. When the bone was recovered from the stream it was dried and usually baked in an oven. It was then crushed into a powder and kept in a sealed container. Small amounts were often mixed in a bottle with linseed or olive oil. In this way you could put some on your finger or on a hanky and wipe it onto the nose or muzzle of the horse. This, it was said, would give the horseman absolute control over his horses.

Many horsemen did not powder the bone but used it whole after it was dried. It was usually wrapped in a special piece of fabric, usually linen, and was then carried around every day as the horseman never knew when it was going to be needed.

Midnight Medicine

Some men carried the bone unwrapped in their armpit for days or weeks at a time so that it became impregnated with the body odour of the man. To make a horse stand still without moving, which was known as jading, they would touch the animal on the shoulder with the bone and to release it they would touch the animal on the rump. It was said to work as the horse could detect without the bone being cured the smell of the dead toad which it detested and feared.

It was also sometimes apparently used when powdered and cured to mix in small quantities in a sick horse's feed where it was supposed to be amazingly beneficial to the animal's health.

Most of these horsemen believed in the supernatural aspects of the ceremony which they thought conferred occult powers to the man over the animal. However, the real reason the bone seemed to work was something Roger was not able to tell me, as even when full of beer the old horsemen were not willing to tell the full story. After the bone was cured and dried and ground into a powder, different herbs and chemicals would be blended into the bony material which gave it a distinctive and significant odour which only the horse with its super sense of smell could detect. If the smell was offensive to the horse such as pig muck, blood or anything organically dead that was enough to freeze the animal into immobility. If the smell was attractive to the horse such as herbs like rosemary, fennel, thyme and many others, the bone could be used to attract the horse and would even make catching the beast in a large field look very easy to interested bystanders who didn't know or understand the secret.

Every man in different districts probably had a different method for curing the bone. One Norfolk horseman described his method of curing the bone to attract the horse. He was taught this method by his father who in turn would have learnt it from his. He placed the bone in the cooling bread oven

Vet for Hire

wrapped in brown paper. The bone was dried out and when it was ready it was pounded into a powder and mixed with some oat flour and olive oil so it formed a cake and baked again in a cooling oven. When it was ready a few drops of rhodium oil (rose oil) was added and the cake was sweated under the horseman's armpit for a few days, after which it was ready for use.

Like other animals most horses are aware when their handler is frightened or tense. A man with a toad's bone in his pocket or material which has the bone in it would be supremely confident in his ability to handle and dominate a large, heavy horse which could be up to a ton in weight. The horse is aware of this confidence and acts accordingly, becoming quietly submissive.

Sometimes the 'magical material' was spread on stable doors, lintels or on harness which. If the odour was repellent the horse would stop eating and be reluctant to work. A horseman would sometimes use these methods if he had a grudge against a farmer or colleague and wanted to make life difficult for them

When Roger was telling me about the Moon men it seemed to him to be a bit of a lark and a youthful prank, but there is no doubt that many horsemen took the ritual very seriously and believed the Devil had been invoked. I heard of one man who had terrible nightmares after he had gone through the ritual. He had a persistent dream that his stallion was coming to his bedside as he slept. He told his wife who was no doubt fed up with having her sleep disturbed. She said nothing had gone right in the house since he had 'truck with the Devil' and told him to get rid of the bone. He dug a large hole and filled a tin box with milk and vinegar. The bone was placed in the box, placed in the hole and covered with heavy clay soil. The man had no more bad dreams after this and his wife was pleased but he never again had the same rapport with his horses. No doubt his self-confidence around his animals had been buried along with the bone.

The superstitious rite known as the 'Water of the Moon' while a secret ritual was fairly well known among horsemen throughout East Anglia and would often be talked about when tongues were loosened by beer, although very few knew the full story. The general public were unaware of what was going on and would only see horsemen with an often uncanny gift for handling horses. Many of the horsemen were also called horse whisperers as they would whisper 'magic words' into the horse's ear. It was possession of the magic word which they said gave them power over the horse. This was said in order to conceal their real methods from the gullible general public.

Norfolk men were close to the land and their horses and these Moon men were enacting rituals which were not only centuries old but possibly dated back as far as Anglo Saxon pagan times. These links are still there and if you scratch the surface and buy an old farmer a pint as I did he might tell you a tale which will make your hair stand on end. Whether you believe it or not I shall leave up to you.

As much as I would like in some ways to go back to the golden days of the heavy horse, I'm glad I have never had to cope with the myths and superstitions that surrounded their handling and treatment. On reflection I will gladly put up with the seeming inconvenience of recording medical details for modern treatments, even if it does mean the occasional drip of water down the back of my neck.

Chapter Eleven
Bread and Butter

One of the aspects of veterinary medicine which attracted me as a young man was the vet's 'fire brigade role.' I relished responding to emergency calls where your presence often made all the difference between life and death for an animal. There was a tremendous adrenaline rush to flying out the clinic door, into the car, breaking many speed limits (in those days the police were remarkably tolerant of speeding vets) and arriving at the scene where everybody was waiting for you in hopeful anticipation that something could be done to save their beast(s).

It was all very exciting and good for a young man's ego but I very quickly came to realise that there was a very fine dividing line between looking like a smart and in control professional and a complete idiot. It was a tightrope on which you balanced precariously every time you responded to a cow calving, a bullock choking on a potato or a horse with colic. Living life on the edge seemed to be what veterinary life was all about but I soon found that as with most jobs it was the day to day routine of life – the bread and butter jobs – which made the practice profitable and paid the wages.

One of the routine jobs which I quite enjoyed was disbudding calves. This means removing the horn buds before they had a chance to grow. It was a very familiar procedure which I knew well from my days growing up on the farm. Each patient is given an injection of local anaesthetic into and around the cornual nerve. This is easy to find as it runs from the corner of the eye up to the horn bud. The local anaesthetic completely takes away the pain which would otherwise be excruciating from using a red-hot disbudding iron. This is needed to burn out and remove the horn buds from both sides of the animal's head. There is usually a pungent smell of burning hair and horn material similar to that produced by a farrier when shoeing horses.

We either used an electric disbudding iron which was very convenient providing there was an electric point close to hand, but as there often wasn't we also had an iron that was heated by bottled gas. The flames from the iron fuelled by the gas would form a ring around the base of the disbudder and could look very alarming. Great care had to be taken not to set anything in the calf shed alight during the procedure – including the patient. The calves did not suffer at all when the horn buds were removed and I was glad to do it as I hated dehorning adult cattle. Adult horns are removed as cattle in groups can do each other great damage with their 'weapons' when competing for food or even saying 'just get out of my way.' Dehorning adult cattle is a bloody and brutal business. The animals are usually restrained in a cattle crush and injected with local anaesthetic in a very similar way to calves for disbudding. After waiting about twenty minutes for the anaesthetic to work the operation begins when the vet reaches for a butchers saw or horn shears and the horns are removed as quickly as possible. You have to remove the horn quite low down on the head both for aesthetic effect and to stop it re-growing. As soon as cutting begins blood flows in copious amounts which once the operation is complete has to be stopped with artery forceps or a cauterising iron, but it is always messy.

I will never forget when the Ayrshire dairy cows at home were dehorned. I was still in my early teens but I vividly remember two vets coming out to do the job. Mr Robinson and Mr McCrone, the vets from the local practice . Each vet started their work at the top of the byre. Mr Robinson took the left side and Mr McCrone the right. The cows were tied up in standings, two to a stall in parallel rows. The byre contained thirty milking cows, all with big horns! They first

Vet for Hire

injected all the animals with local anaesthetic. By the time they had finished injecting all the cows it was time to start at the beginning again at the top of the building. They had one farm hand holding each beast in turn with bull dog clamps fitted into the nostrils to restrain them. The vets went from cow to cow with saw in hand virtually without pausing. It must have been quite a marathon for them. No attempt was made to stop the bleeding. I was told it was unnecessary. The noise, mess and smell from the distressed animals lives with me still. It was horrible. The pristine white walls of the byre were covered in blood as were the vets, handlers and animals. But truth to say the bleeding did stop and the cows, although down in milk yield by about a third at the afternoon milking, were back to normal the next day. Looking back I'm surprised it didn't put me off wanting to be a vet for life.

I have in my turn dehorned many adult cattle – it was part of the job but I always hated it and have always been pleased to disbud calves as it saved them from the awful business when they were adults. Disbudding calves is now one of those jobs which vets do very rarely as farmers are now trained to do the job themselves. It's cheaper that way.

Disbudding goats is a much more complicated business. Kids' horn buds cannot be anaesthetised easily with local anaesthetic. The nerve supply to the horn is much more complex than in calves and my practice policy was always to get goat owners to bring their kids into the clinic for disbudding as I wanted to do the operation when they were only a few days old and when the horn bud was not too big. Every little animal was given a sedative injection which tended to make it sleep for hours. Because the kids took so long to recover I later modified this protocol to giving the youngsters a gaseous anaesthetic from which they recovered very quickly. Because of the use of the hot iron it was unnecessary to prepare the operation site in the normal way as the heat cauterised any possible infection. One of my colleagues forgot this one day

Bread and Butter

and cleaned the area using surgical spirit which caused instant ignition as soon as the iron was applied and the kid had a few singed hairs and the vet acute palpitations. All was well but it was one of the hazards of disbudding kids. Applying the iron too long to the bud was another. Young goats have very thin cranial bones and if the hot iron is applied for the same length of time as for a calf then it is possible to cause brain damage to the youngster. One to two seconds at a time is long enough. Damaged kids never happened on my watch but I had heard of such cases in other practices. Disbudding kids despite the hazards is still worthwhile compared to dehorning adult goats which is even more difficult than the operation in adult cattle.

Castrating animals was another routine job which could take up a large part of my day. It was commonplace to be sent out by the boss to castrate up to twenty litters of pigs at a time if it was a big pig farm. Piglets would vary in age from a few days old to three or four weeks old and no anaesthetic was involved. The tedium of the job was only relieved by dodging the enraged mother sows that would often try and leap over any intervening pens to get at the vet who was hurting her babies. Young pigs squeal at a very high pitch just when they are being caught and held and the noise goes up an octave during the procedure which is fortunately over very quickly. Thankfully it's not a job that is done very much now at all as pigs, due to improved diets and growth rates, reach slaughter weight before the testosterone in their system taints the meat which was the justification for the castration in the first place.

The same is true for male calves that were often faced with the double whammy of disbudding and castrating at the same time. Young animals get over castration very quickly but older animals take a few days. I used to be asked to castrate quite old barley beef cattle which could be quite hazardous. Local anaesthetic was injected into each testicle with the animal usually in a cattle crush. The vet was very likely to get kicked either giving the injection or during the operation which was

Vet for Hire

made all the more dangerous by having both a syringe and a needle in your hand or a very sharp scalpel blade. The trick to avoid too much damage to your anatomy was to get very close to the animal's leg so that if it was going to kick, the leg and hoof would have a very short trajectory and would be less likely to hurt too much. All the same I would often come back from a job with one or both legs black and blue with bruises, which I suppose was fair enough considering what I was doing to them.

Another very regular job in a dairy practice was cleansing cows. This involved removing any retained after birth once the cow had calved. A cow will normally expel the placenta within a few hours of calving but many do not and it is then the vet's job to remove it manually.

It was normal practice to carry out the procedure within three to five days after the calving, depending on the individual farmer's whim and the vet's practice protocol. A retained after birth will eventually cause a metritis (an infection in the uterus) which if left untreated could be fatal or might result in infertility and an inability of getting the cow in calf again. Bovine placenta is attached to the lining of the uterus by large mushroom like cotyledons and the vet with his hand and arm inside the cow must detach the membranes from each mushroom. It can be a long and arduous job and I learned to use both right and left hands in turn when one got tired. The very first cow I 'cleansed' was as a student and it was on a cousin's farm when he was not at home. My boss thought it was too good a chance not to let the student have a go and learn the job, but he kept looking around the cow shed door to see whether the owner was going to turn up and tell me to hurry up. With all the placenta removed the last job was always to put some antibiotic pessaries into the uterus then flick them one handed to the deepest recesses of the womb to make sure that any risk of infection was avoided. It was often quite difficult to make sure all the membranes were removed but the cows were usually very resilient and, providing you got at least 98% out and put the pessaries in, then all would normally be well.

This is not the case with mares. The placenta in the mare is attached to every part of the lining of the uterus and failure to remove every last bit of membrane would be disastrous. It's a bit like peeling a very thin friable orange one handed in a large wet sack – and blindfold! In addition there is the extra hazard of standing at the back of the mare that may well be very agitated, having just given birth and very liable to kick. In the absence of stocks, which is most of the time, the mare has to be backed up to a half shut stable door and the vet stands on the other side which provides some protection.

The placenta must be removed within hours of giving birth and if it is not then the mare will get toxic shock, metritis and laminitis. Many have died due to retained placenta and the usual procedure after every cleansing is to examine every bit of the afterbirth to make sure you have got it all and knowledgeable owners will inspect it with you. There is no room for error.

Even with a waterproof gown, disposable gloves and sleeves it's a smelly and messy job whether it is a cow or a mare and the odour tends to linger with you for the rest of the day which is never good if you have afternoon appointments with small animal clients.

One of the very regular jobs a vet has to do is to certify a document is correct. It can be as simple as a vaccination certificate or more complex as with a death certificate for insurance purposes.

No matter what you are signing as a vet it has to be correct to the best of your knowledge and belief. Signing a document you know to be wrong will get the vet involved in very hot

Vet for Hire

water indeed with the Royal College of Veterinary Surgeons and could get the person in question struck off and disbarred from veterinary practice.

It can be a very simple matter. Horse flu vaccination certificates have to be correct to the day. If they are so much as a day overdue the vaccine course has to start again which is expensive. I've lost count of the number of times I have been asked to put the wrong date on a certificate. The common response by the client to the request that has been turned down is to say 'nobody will know.'

My reply was always that "I would know and you would know and I'm sorry but I won't do it." It can be difficult for a young vet to resist these types of demand as refusal might mean the loss of a client but it has to be done. One of the last times I was asked to do it was by the wife of a solicitor and she was distinctly miffed at my refusal. She could not see what the problem was and went back and reported to her husband, expecting him to have the same reaction as herself. He was horrified and pointed out the error of her ways. She did phone me later to apologise.

Certificates have to be given for many different reasons. It used to be very common after a thunder storm to be asked to certify a death – usually a grazing animal – as the result of a lightning strike. This type of death is usually covered by insurance.

It's quite easy to certify this if there has been evidence of an electric storm and scorch marks are found on the animal's skin. Lack of evidence means the certificate cannot be given which again will upset a client. The only way forward from this type of impasse has to be a full post mortem which the client has to pay for and which may or may not prove the case.

One of the strangest requests which I had to turn down did

not involve a certificate but had I agreed would have involved me in fraud. A farmer phoned and asked to come urgently to shoot a bullock which he said was dying from bloat.

When I got to the farm I found the animal dead with its throat cut. I was then asked to shoot the dead bullock so that it could be taken to the slaughter house as a casualty as if it had been shot and bled on the farm. On farm slaughter was quite legal in certain circumstances involving casualty animals if the correct procedures were followed. A good example of this would be where a beast has a broken leg and must not be subjected to transporting to an abattoir because of the pain it would suffer. It was permissible in those types of circumstances for the animal to be killed humanely and bled properly on the farm, observing all the necessary hygienic precautions. An animal that has died from natural causes no matter what the cause must not be taken to a slaughter house and must on no account be used for human consumption. It is illegal and if I had agreed to do as the farmer requested and put a bullet hole in the skull I would not only have been struck off but could have been jailed for fraud.

I think what had happened was that the bullock had died some hours before and in order to try and compensate himself for his loss the farmer cut the dead animal's throat and then tried to persuade me to participate in his deception. He wasn't surpised that I flatly turned down his request but we never had the same rapport again and a few months later he moved on to another practice – to my relief.

Most routine farm visits for vets are now very much in an advisory role and in doing health and fertility testing. Farm records on progressive farms are now computerised and a lot of time can be spent evaluating and assessing data. Livestock farms must be run efficiently if they are to survive and a modern veterinary practice must be very aware of this and have computer health programmes to match these very

Vet for Hire

necessary aspirations. I got my first insight into this from my brother who twenty years ago was a dairy farmer. He proudly demonstrated his new computer system which could tell him while he lay in bed at five in the morning when the cows were being milked and whether an animal needed attention or not. It worked very well. It simply told him when a cow – each one had a number on a collar around her neck which responded to the computer – did not eat all her ration when she was being milked. It would also tell him if the individual was down on her previous day's milk yield. This data would be enough to tell him to make a point of checking an individual animal. The cow might simply have come into season or have mastitis but she would need to be checked. It was an aide to assist the dairyman who had well over a hundred cows to feed and milk. A computer can never take the place of a good stockman but there is little doubt it is an invaluable tool in making sure larger farms are run well and efficiently.

Vetting horses or ponies for purchase causes every equine vet a certain amount of anxiety, especially if the animal involved is worth a lot of money. Originally a vet would examine the animal that was being purchased on behalf of his client and if the animal was fit for purchase he or she would sign a document after writing a description of the horse that *"I hereby certify that this horse (or pony) is sound in wind, eyes, heart and action."* In other words it was either perfect or it was not without any shades of grey. I signed a few of these documents when I first started as a young vet and I always did it with my heart in my mouth as no animal is perfect – not even a Derby winner.

Fortunately the system was changed into a well structured programme involving a five stage examination where the principle is that the vet examines the animal at rest, trotting out which should show up any lameness and followed by ridden exercise to make the horse or pony work really hard. There is then a final examination afterwards allowing the animal to recover from its exertions. At this stage a blood sample is taken in case the horse has been given a drug to mask any signs of lameness or any other defect. Many vets will, in addition if the horse is worth lots of money, take X-rays of the animal's legs and feet as extra insurance against getting a decision wrong.

It is very unusual not to find some defect or imperfection and if I found absolutely nothing wrong with any particular horse I would look even harder. The certificate allows the vet to list any abnormalities or problems and then give an opinion as to whether the animal is suitable for purchase to be used as the new owner would wish. It's a much better way of examining a horse for soundness but it still causes the examining vet anxiety in case he or she misses some obvious problem and gets sued.

One of the last soundness examinations my late revered partner Alec Noble did before he retired was a horse that was going to be used for show jumping and cross country events. All was well at the time of examination and Alec put the animal through its paces, including jumping a few fences and found no problem. Unfortunately within two weeks of purchase the animal went lame and Alec got the blame for passing it as sound. It did not go to court and he was completely vindicated in his opinion but I knew he had a few sleepless nights until the matter was resolved.

I used to ride the occasional horse when I examined it for purchase but stopped after a particular episode. The animal was owned by my client and she wanted me to ride it to listen for any defects in its breathing while it was galloping. I think she set me up as I was never a brilliant rider but was always prepared to have a go. The animal was a sixteen hand bay gelding and no sooner had I got into the saddle when it took off across a stubble field as if it was pursuing a very lively pack of hell hounds on a mission. It was a large field with a very big ditch at the far end which the horse and I were approaching

Vet for Hire

at a ridiculous speed. I just about managed to get it turned around without getting chucked off and we came back at a flat out gallop. My main problem was to stop the beast and get off without losing too much dignity. Listening to the respiratory noise, which after all had been the whole point of the exercise, was totally lost on me as I was much too busy trying to stay on the horse's back to bother about anything else. I survived – red faced and breathing heavily – but very aware I had made a bit of a fool of myself. I should never have agreed to the client's request, although my equestrian skills (or lack of them) did make her laugh. At least the episode made me aware that the gelding needed an experienced rider and not a rank amateur like me. I learned the hard way that it is much better and safer when doing a soundness examination to listen to a horse's respiratory noises from the safety of the ground where you can listen properly without any distractions.

'Bread and butter' is all very well but in veterinary practice life is often not straightforward and the 'jam' of excitement is never too far away.

Chapter Twelve
Home and Away

For most people in the UK when it comes to animal welfare there is one organisation which is top of the list and that is the RSPCA (Royal Society for the Prevention of Cruelty to Animals). It was founded in 1824 by a group of reformers and was the first animal welfare society and charity to be founded in the world. It was granted royal status in 1840 by Queen Victoria and its first notable success led to the abolition of bear baiting. There are now many different charities and organisations in the UK dedicated to the care and welfare of farm animals, horses and domestic pets. Some are aimed at particular species such as the Cats' Protection League and World Horse Welfare but very many are just run by private people with a passion for caring. Many individuals volunteer to give their lives (and even occasionally their fortunes) to the cause and do wonderful work. This can sometimes be misguided and more harm can be done than good but on balance the welfare of animals in this country is watched over with care and dedication.

When I went to work for a time in Hong Kong I was interested and concerned about the standards of care given to stray animals. How did the average person living in Hong Kong feel about their pets and animals in general? The Chinese have a reputation for disregarding animals' feelings and physical care, a reputation fuelled by horrific stories of the treatment of honey bears kept in cages to be 'milked' for their bile, eating dogs and animals being skinned alive for their fur.

When I first arrived in Hong Kong I rather assumed that the SPCA (they dropped the Royal bit after the 1997 handover)

Vet for Hire

would be in pole position when it came to animal rescue and rehoming. I found to my surprise that the SPCA had many clinics all over Hong Kong and was actually in competition for business with all the other private veterinary clinics in the city. As a result they did not always endear themselves to their business rivals as more and more private clinics struggled for an ever diminishing slice of the business cake. In their defence the SPCA say that their services are available to members only but the reality is that anyone can walk into an SPCA clinic and for a small fee sign up and then receive discounted appropriate treatment and medication from a qualified vet. All proceeds and profits after paying wages and expenses go to support the welfare work of the Society. They need the income to continue their work as unlike their counterparts in the UK the SPCA does not get a large income from donations.

The Society have an adoption centre in Wan Chai and a smaller one in Mong Kok but with the size of the stray population of both dogs and cats they on their own cannot hope to cope. Inspectors are available as in the UK to respond to calls to collect or rescue strays and investigate cruelty cases but as I was soon to learn all too well from personal knowledge due to overwork and probably too few inspectors the reality on the street is sometimes far from ideal. A client of the practice where I was working reported a case of an old dog on a very short chain to the nearest SPCA clinic. The animal was in the scalding hot sun without shade and water and the client was told by staff that nothing could be done for twenty four to thirty six hours. The situation was resolved quickly and easily by reporting the matter to the police who investigated immediately and were able to get an SPCA inspector on the scene straight away.

Stray dogs that are reported causing a nuisance are not reported to the SPCA but are instead collected and caught by Ministry officials and put down if they cannot be identified. All dogs over six months of age in Hong Kong should be by law vaccinated against rabies and have a micro chip implanted at the same time. The owner is then issued with a license. Any stray dog is kept for 3 days and if no owner is found the animal is killed. I was aware of clients who had their two German Shepherd dogs escape through an open gate. They failed to find them in time as both animals were euthanased just thirty minutes before the owners turned up at the dog pound. Red tape and officials had delayed them but they alone were to blame as the dogs were unlicensed and not micro chipped. Still, it must have been devastating to be just too late to save both young healthy dogs.

Fortunately for the many abandoned and stray cats and dogs in Hong Kong there are many other rescue societies just like in the UK. An overstretched SPCA alone could not possibly cope.

In 1998 co founders El Chan and Noel Fan set up a society called the Society for Abandoned Animals (SAA) and a sanctuary was established up near the Chinese border at Yeun Long on what was formerly a pig farm. The two women were partners in a pet grooming business and were being driven to despair by the number of animals (mostly dogs) that were being abandoned on their premises and on the streets. Both women hated to see healthy animals being put to sleep. The motto of the organisation became: "Care and Respect Never Kill Never abandon."

As the motto stated they never killed a healthy animal.

On one of my days off I paid a visit to the shelter as I had heard so much (all of it good) about the establishment. It took about two hours travelling time on the local bus and seemed to me to be fiendishly difficult to get to. I was taken along by Sze Sze (pronounced See See) who was one of the nurses in the clinic where I worked. She helped out on a voluntary basis at the sanctuary about twice a month and assisted the vet with

Vet for Hire

treatments and minor operations.

The day I visited there were over three hundred dogs as well as cats housed in a separate part of the building together with a few domestic rabbits, two chickens, two fully grown pigs and four goats. Nothing was turned away.

The SAA has re-homed many animals (they call it re-birth) in the time they have been established. As happens in the UK all new potential owners are vetted thoroughly by a trained volunteer before they are allowed to take away a pet and a follow up visit to the new home is mandatory.

The running costs of such a large shelter are huge. Even out in a very rural location the rent was H/K $30.000 per month. Staff wages have to be paid too and all veterinary expenses even when done at cost price have to be met. It was the largest shelter in Hong Kong and the need seems to be increasing all the time. To keep going is a constant struggle to keep up standards and the Chinese have a saying: "I know at last what distinguishes man from animals – financial worries."

There are apparently over one hundred rescue organisations in Hong Kong and as in Britain many are started for the best of reasons but the people running the shelters often have bigger hearts than pockets and many close down after a very short time. This inevitably causes even more distress to the inmates who have to be re-homed again or put down by Government officials.

No such fate is likely to await the dogs in the rescue kennels run by Mr Ng who I mentioned earlier. He was and I presume still is a client of the practice in Sai Kung where I worked and a very wealthy man. He needed to be as he would take in and look after any stray dog he could find. He started out by keeping dogs he had rescued at his home but very rapidly ran out of space and everything grew very rapidly so that in just over six years he had three separate shelters all within a few hundred metres of each other, each containing over sixty dogs. He has staff living at each shelter. A husband and wife team live in a bungalow next to one premises and two men look after the others. In addition he has a foreman/driver who is in overall charge and brings any animals requiring attention into the clinic.

All the premises are kept in pristine condition. The paintwork is fresh and faeces are collected almost as they drop. All the animals are micro-chipped and vaccinated against rabies as required by law. They have their routine vaccinations and are protected against heartworm and intestinal worms on a routine basis. On my last working day in Hong Kong I vaccinated twenty five dogs and dosed every animal with revolution which is used for heartworm protection and against intestinal worms. The monthly cost to Mr Ng must be huge. His second overflow kennels when set up cost H/K $800.000 just to buy and renovate.

Why does he do it? I'm not really sure. He is a very self effacing man who hates publicity and his English and my Cantonese were not up to asking these kinds of questions. He is very hands on with his rescue organisation despite having textile and shipping businesses to run in Hong Kong and Mainland China. Each morning when he is not away on business he is down in Sai Kung feeding strays and if he finds an animal in distress then he or one of his staff will catch it, get it treated and take it back to one of the shelters. He never re-homes a dog. They are looked after for life and none are put down unless it is absolutely necessary.

He does not take in cats but fortunately some organisations are, like the Cat's Protection League in the UK, run especially for cats. These include Cat Salvation Army and Hong Kong Cats and of course the SAA have a section just for cats. It is never enough but like in the UK enough is never enough.

Vet for Hire

Feral cattle live all over the New Territories in Hong Kong. They are the ancestors of domestic cattle abandoned by farmers when farming ceased in Hong Kong in the 1950s. They are almost all quiet, steady beasts and give no one any trouble apart from when they wander into town as they do from time to time and get in front of vehicles. They seem to manage very well and look very sleek and well fed except in the dry season when the grazing is not so lush. They appear to be able to look after themselves without any human agency to assist them except for those cattle on Lantau Island. A lady there looks after about seventy feral cattle. She does this on a shoestring budget and unlike their counterparts around Sai Kung they are a fairly unhealthy looking bunch. Rumour has it they had Foot and Mouth disease some time ago and never quite recovered. She had herself to be rescued when I was there when she got stuck in some mud or quicksand and could not extricate herself. She was rescued by the superb emergency services. Still she struggles on tending to her 'family' as she sees them. But for her care and dedication the cattle on Lantua would have died out years ago. I'm sure they would be grateful if they only knew. That probably goes for all rescued animals.

George Bernard Shaw said: "The worst sin towards our fellow creatures is not to hate them but to be indifferent to them. That's the essence of inhumanity."

I shouldn't have been surprised that the care of animals in Hong Kong was in many ways similar to that in the UK: one or two large organisations and many small, all doing their best for animal welfare. Hong Kong was after all until recently a British colony and has changed little since the handover to China. They even make sure their retired race horses are well looked after. There were six equine vets in Hong Kong all working for the Hong Kong Jockey Club. It's the job of the sixth vet (paid by the Jockey Club) to visit all the retired horses in both Hong Kong and China just to make sure they are being cared for properly.

Home & Away

This is very different to some other countries a lot closer to home and I spend two weeks and a bit more every year on a Greek island being the island vet for a charity called PAWS (Paxos Animal Welfare Society).

Paxos is a little teardrop of a Greek island about one hour due south of Corfu by fast hydrofoil ferry. It is very small – about seven miles by three at its widest point and covered from top to bottom with olive and cyprus trees. I have had many happy family holidays in Paxos since the early 1980s but my first visit as a working vet was very different. The job is basically to neuter as many feral cats as possible in the time allowed. I am helped in this task by Zoe Tomkinson, a veterinary nurse from Manchester, and we have a remit as well to treat any other dogs, cats, donkeys or goats that might require our help.

I love going every year. As a tourist I had been distressed to see pathetic, scruffy, snuffly little creatures begging at every taverna when I sat down to eat. The evening would inevitably pass with slipping the odd morsel to whatever cat was nearest to hand. They in turn would pass on their fleas and unprotected legs would soon be covered in red itchy spots that the locals would insist were mosquito bites but I was never quite convinced.

PAWS is a charity set up by two English women, Linda Parker and Lindsay Geddes, and up until its foundation the local moggies had a very precarious existence. Every few years the population would build up to a point where in the winter months disease and starvation would overwhelm the weaker animals. In addition the locals were not averse to resorting to poison to keep the numbers in check. Despite this cats are needed and valued by the locals to keep the rats (euphemistically called fruit mice in order not to frighten the tourists) in check. There are only a very few lucky individuals on the island who live as pampered pets.

Vet for Hire

Lindsay and Linda knew there had to be another solution for the Paxos cat problem and this meant an island wide neutering programme. They set up PAWS as a registered charity and started to raise money both in the UK and on Paxos to start the neutering programme.

There is no permanent vet on Paxos. Occasionally a vet from Corfu visits as his mother lives on the island and will see a few animals while he is over for the weekend. Paxiots with pets requiring veterinary assistance normally have to travel to Corfu where prices are roughly comparable to the UK. This, with the added ferry costs, makes even a simple vaccination or neutering very expensive. PAWS pays the travel and accommodation costs for the vet and veterinary nurse to stay on the island for up to four weeks at a time. The team then undertakes to neuter as many cats as possible. The ferals are trapped and collected by volunteers, both Greek and ex pat.

On our first working visit to the island I arranged to meet Zoe and her partner James at the ferry terminal in Corfu. We had flown in by Easyjet from Gatwick and Manchester on their red eye dawn flights. I recognised Zoe by her photo on Facebook and she recognised me as she knew my wife Chris had a broken bone in her foot and was on crutches. Zoe had never been to Greece before but that was to prove no hindrance as we recognised, despite our age differences, that we were kindred spirits on the same wavelength. We were taking over from Jess and Claire who were just finishing a ten day stint and we overlapped by half a day which was very useful. We also 'inherited' two stray kittens that had been dumped in some rubbish bags. There was a lot of that happening on the island. The white one was rapidly christened Dave and the tiny black and white female with lots of attitude was called Doreen.

The clinic was basically not much better than a large garden shed and was situated at the bottom of our apartment garden which was full of olive trees, fruit trees, wild orchids and various cats with tipped ears and a relaxed 'I don't care, I've been done' attitude. The clinic had two rooms with a shower room and toilet attached. The second room had been a bedroom with two single beds still in situ which I think may have been used to house Albanian workers of which there were many on the island. It was small but adequate and was to be our HQ for the duration of our visit. We had been warned that the autoclave which had been brought over at great expense from the UK to sterilise the instruments was not working but we did have two pressure cookers which would do the job. Zoe's partner James seemed to have a degree in DIY and he soon got to work on the autoclave, took it to bits and got it working within hours.

My first day as the island vet got off to an inauspicious start. It was quite quiet which was just as well as I had a touch of food poisoning. Beware clingfilm wrapped ham and cheese sandwiches in Corfu! Goodness knows just how old they had been. I castrated three cats and examined a few other animals brought in for treatment. Worse was to follow. I was asked to euthanase six four day old healthy puppies. It was not something I would ever consider doing in the UK but the alternative was that they were either going to be drowned, abandoned or hit on the head with a shovel. The owner of the bitch was leaving the island on the ferry to return to Athens. He promised me that he would have the bitch sterilised as soon as her milk dried up. I was prepared to be very angry with him but could not as tears were pouring down his cheeks as I made him hold each little creature in turn. He also gave a big contribution to PAWS. We do not charge for veterinary services but have a large notice in both Greek and English asking for donations to help fund the continuing work.

We mostly do not start work until 9.00am, but being in Greece very little happens before 9.30 to 10.00 when the first trickle of people with animals in baskets tend to show up.

Vet for Hire

Most days we will be finished by 2.00pm. After this time the island's population tends to go to sleep unless you are in a tourist bar or taverna until about 6.00pm before which nothing much happens. By late afternoon most of the cats are awake after their operations and ready to go home or be released. We use a triple combo of anaesthetic of domitor, torbugesic and ketamine and we can reverse the anaesthetic with antisedan. We learned very early on not to do this. It was better to let the cats wake naturally as they then do not bother with their wounds. Two cats were going home early so we reversed their anaesthetic and both promptly woke up and took their stitches out. This would not have been possible in the UK as the cats would all have been fitted with buster collars to stop this from happening. Not only did we not have any but any cat with a collar has to be kept indoors until the wound heals which is not something you can do with wild cats.

Every operated cat has a health check, mostly while asleep which is not ideal, but most are feral and have to be injected in a crush cage. All have droncit injections for worms, pain relief and are treated for fleas. We put a V shaped nick in every feral cat's left ear but not if the animal is owned by a Greek. It is seen as unnecessary mutilation. This seemed a bit strange until I was told that in a previous year another vet had been rather enthusiastic about cropping the ears of sterilised cats and one had bled for days. Word gets around very quickly on a small island where everybody knows everybody and their business.

Since PAWS went to Paxos we tried to go to outlying villages where feral cats are a very large problem. Lakka was a particularly difficult area as the local cat lady (Yvonne) who feeds all the strays would let out any animals that had been trapped for neutering. When it comes to cats in Lakka Yvonne's word is law. She has always been against neutering, especially male cats as she believes it is unnatural and makes male cats lazy and less good at hunting. This last year, however, led to a breakthrough as Yvonne phoned me and asked us to go to

Lakka. She arranged that we should meet at the Old School House and she would as many cats as possible to come for neutering.

We arrived at 10.00am to find cats and owners arriving but the school doors were firmly locked. There were no tables or chairs, no electricity, no water and no Yvonne. I went to the next door (Italian) taverna and asked for a table.

"We closed – no food," came the response.

"No, no I don't want to eat. Can I borrow a table, and two chairs as well would be nice."

"Oh borrow! OK – no problem."

I staggered back to the School with the equipment to find a Greek local had arrived with five gallons of clean water. Another had illegally plugged our extension cable into a power source on the outside wall of the building. We could now use the autoclave and the clippers and get started. Best of all Yvonne arrived with three cats trotting behind her like little dogs.

We began the operations very soon after and working without a break by 4.15pm we had spayed 17 cats and removed a cancerous ear. The only pause we allowed ourselves was when we had to move the 'operating table' into the shade and when we had a non-alcoholic drink between procedures. Yvonne spent her day stroking the unconscious cats and talking to them in Greek. But true to form no tom cats came to be castrated. Yvonne's law still held sway. Tom cats in Lakka are still safe to fight and procreate and spread disease for another year but perhaps next year might be different?

Not all outside venues were as austere as Lakka. One of my favourite places is a small cafe bar in Magazia owned

Vet for Hire

by Costa. We operate under a vine leaf canopy in the garden using two round metal pub style tables. One is the prep table and the other for the operations and I sit on a bar seat while I perform. Scrubbing hands pre op is easy but I have to kneel at the garden tap which is a bit hard on my bony knees as I'm wearing shorts because of the heat. We have a constant and changing audience of Greeks who sit at adjoining tables in a semi circle around us drinking their ouzo and coffee. It always seems to me to be a bit like being in a talent show and both Zoe and I expect to be rewarded with points for style or for dealing with a particularly vicious feral. Costa usually keeps us well supplied with drinks and on our last visit we stopped for lunch – on the house courtesy of our welcoming host.

In addition to the neutering program I attend to any animal that is brought along by a concerned owner. Dogs in Greece and Paxos have a high incidence of Leishmaniasis which is caused by a protozoan parasite transmitted by sand flies. It is a particularly nasty illness which can go on for years and the treatment has to be prolonged and is very expensive. Quite a few of the locals approached me to see if I could dispense the treatment required. I could not and it was very difficult to see sick animals not getting the correct medication due to the owners not being able to afford the costs of the drug. Two other owners had dogs that were in remission but needed the drugs to keep their animals healthy and again could not afford the treatment. On every occasion all I could advise was to go to the Corfu vets for treatment and try and obtain the correct medication via the internet.

Goats on Paxos climb trees. I'm not sure whether it is characteristic of the island's goats or a commonplace occurrence everywhere in the Mediterranean. The fact that they climb trees also means the occasional animal will fall out of a tree, resulting in lameness at best or a fractured limb at worst. During my stay we have not yet had a goat with a broken leg but I suspect a Greek local that owns a goat with a fractured bone would rapidly solve the problem by creating 'lamb' kebabs for the tourists to eat.

There are two wild donkeys which periodically walk through Gaois, the main village on the island, always in line astern and always with the jenny leading the jack. They ignore all traffic and look quite healthy but I was phoned by a tourist who was worried as she had seen blood splashes on the male donkey's back. This was almost certainly the result of fly bites and I would have loved to be able to sprinkle louse and flea powder on its back but I did not have the treatment or the means of getting anywhere near the patient as they run like hell, kicking and biting if anyone tries to catch them. Perhaps they heard a rumour about donkey kebabs or worse still, being harnessed to transport the local corpulent priest.

It's always a bit difficult to know whether as outsiders we are totally welcome on the island. We understand concerns from the older inhabitants that neutering cats will deplete the population too much but there was no doubt the PAWS T-shirt is recognised throughout the island and almost universally greeted with smiles of approval. This was confirmed to me one evening when I was walking though a back lane in Gaois about to go shopping. A little Greek girl, probably about eight or nine years old, ran up behind me and pointing at me, or was it the shirt, cried out, "Vet, vet."

I said, "Yes, yes," and she gave me a double thumbs up sign and a cheeky grin and said, "Good, good." I saw her a couple of days later when with a friend she brought her dog in for a check up and gave us a five euro donation for PAWS. The dog was fit and well and just needed some worm tablets and flea treatment.

It's a very different experience from being a tourist to living and working in a foreign country, even for just a short time every year. I'm not very good at lying on a beach and working

Vet for Hire

for a few hours every day suits me very well and is a way of repaying Paxos' people for all the good times and happy memories I have had over the many years I visited as a tourist.

The last time we left Paxos it was very early in the morning. It was a very misty pink tinged sunrise which promised another beautiful day. As the boat nudged out from the harbour I saw a pod of dolphins, both young and old, playing and jumping around the boat. As we picked up speed they kept pace with the hydrofoil and were surfing through the bow waves on either side of us. They were like children, cavorting, playing, showing off and having fun. In all the years I have been travelling to Greece it was the first time I had seen dolphins. It was a wonderful finale to our stay and my only regret was that my camera was safely tucked away in my suitcase where it could not be reached. Ah well, there is always next year.

Chapter Thirteen
Vet for Hire....Still

When I came back from Hong Kong I spent a couple of years in gainful salaried employment but I have now slipped the bonds of my monthly pay cheque and rejoined the ranks of the self employed. It might seem a stupid move given the dire economic climate at the moment but I am reminded that I am now of 'pensionable age' despite feeling younger in attitude than I did when I was twenty or thirty. I am not one to deceive myself that sixty is the new fifty (or is it the other way round, I can never quite remember?) but I will admit to a desire not to be on regular emergency call outs at nights and weekends. This in itself may be a symptom of getting older and decrepit but perhaps not. I know very many of my younger colleagues who have professed a similar desire, despite most vets agreeing that as a profession it is vital we continue to offer a twenty four hour emergency service throughout the year.

Working with younger vets is one of the great rewards of ageing within a small profession. The ebb and flow of experience exchanged for new techniques and knowledge is for me vital in the process of keeping up to date and just as important as formal continuing professional development. I have, however, to be careful when in conversation not to find myself sliding down the slippery slope into yet another boring veterinary anecdote and finding my audience glassy eyed with wonder, but more likely boredom. It's very easy to look back over forty years, as I can, to the diseases, surgical techniques and treatments of that time and to realise now, in the light of present day knowledge, how wrong we were about so many things. But as I tell my younger colleagues, much of what we think and do know will almost certainly be looked on as antiquated and useless in another fifty years time.

Vet for Hire

However, there are some things that I was taught as a young vet student that are still relevant and correct today. A good illustration of this occurred whilst I was writing this book. A rather old cat that would not see ten years of age again was presented with a very swollen abdomen and vaginal discharge. The very obvious conclusion was that she must have a pyometra. In lay terms this means a swollen uterus full of purulent material. When questioned the owner said that she had rescued her some years before from a welfare organisation and had been assured that the cat had been neutered. Since then she had never been in season and never had kittens. A blood sample showed only a small rise in her white cell count which would indicate a mild infection only, and her blood biochemistry parameters were all within normal range. She was not drinking excessively and was still eating but with a reduced appetite.

Fearing the worst – possibly an abdominal tumour – I took a couple of X-rays before an ultra sound scan which showed a twin horned uterus full to overflowing with pus. After speaking to the owner I performed an exploratory abdominal operation. Both horns of the uterus were very big and distended, taking up most of the abdomen. There were no ovaries. Both had been removed, presumably when the cat was neutered some years before, possibly when she was only a few months old, leaving her womb as a useless and empty organ just waiting to become infected. I do remember very clearly being lectured by Professor Jimmy Spreull, then head of surgery at the Royal Dick School of Veterinary Medicine, never to do this (ie. ovariectomy without hysterectomy) as the consequence would be the very thing which I was now seeing. It only took forty years for his words to ring true. I understand from colleagues that vets are again being trained to remove just the ovaries when an animal is neutered as this can be done through a much smaller wound and is less invasive. We are being told that this technique carries no greater risk to the animal of post operation complications but I for one do not believe it and will carry on removing both the ovaries and uterus when I spay a cat or a bitch. Sometimes, just sometimes, the old ways are the best ways and this old cat made a good recovery, much to the owner's pleasure and relief.

There are many diseases that are now commonly diagnosed that were completely unknown (at least to me) when I first graduated. Cushing's disease is one that springs all too readily to mind. Dogs with the condition drink and eat excessively and have large, pendulous abdomens. Their skin becomes very thin and they begin to look a bit bald. It's common enough now and comparatively easy to diagnose by clinical signs and blood tests, but I shudder to think to just how many dogs my then colleagues and I unknowingly gave the disease due to the careless and prolonged use of steroids for the treatment of chronic, itchy skins. Betsolan tablets were wonderful for stopping a dog scratching lumps out of itself but their overuse, we came to realise, had very serious consequences. Cushing's disease is the result of too much steroid in the body which, if the disease occurs naturally, is caused by a tumour in the adrenal gland or the pituitary gland in the brain. We seem to diagnose more and more dogs with this condition than ever before and it can't now be overuse of steroids. It's much more likely that the clinical antennae are more primed and sensitive to detecting more of the same. It was certainly the case when we had a locum one summer for a few weeks. Peter seemed to blood test almost every other dog and the incidence of the disease appeared to rise rapidly.

The same may be true for hyperthyroidism in cats. It is mostly older cats that develop the condition. They become hyperactive, and despite eating lots of food get very thin. The disease was unknown in my early veterinary years and its clinical signs were often attributed – without the benefit of in-house blood testing machines – to kidney failure. Very many cats were destroyed on that premise as we did not know any better. Even if we did the medication was not available for

Vet for Hire

treatment. I sometimes wonder what other conditions are lying hidden, waiting to be discovered and successfully treated. No doubt there are very many which our as yet unborn veterinary colleagues will treat as a matter of course and wonder at our present veterinary ignorance.

Some diseases come and go and seem almost to be cyclical in some respects. It's easy to understand why allergic skin conditions are more common in the summer months when there is a lot of pollen about, and colic in horses in the winter months as the result of constipation and a bad diet. But why does it happen that I can go for months without diagnosing a blocked bladder in a neutered male cat and suddenly, out of the blue can see three cases in a week?

The same could be said for many other diseases such as pyometra in bitches and lameness, mostly in dogs as the result of torn cruciate ligaments in the knee. You can bet your veterinary life on it that if you do cruciate surgery on a dog you will most likely have another similar procedure to perform within a week or two at the most.

Other diseases and conditions have briefly flared across the veterinary firmament and now, like the hole in the ozone layer, have virtually disappeared. A condition I well remember for being very common about thirty years ago was Key – Gaskell (Feline dysautonomia). Cats with the disease do not eat, regurgitate and have dilated pupils which are unresponsive to light. Treatment can be very difficult and it's a disease very similar to Grass sickness in horses where the bowel becomes paralysed. No one really knows what caused the problem in cats (or horses for that matter). There are many theories but no firm conclusion as to the aetiology, but for me the disease has virtually disappeared, although I have no doubt that a colleague somewhere will be able to tell of just such a diagnosis only last week. The same could be said for Transmissible Gastro Enteritis (T.G.E) and Vomiting and Wasting disease in piglets.

Vet for Hire....Still

When I was a much younger vet and concerned with such matters on pig farms, the diagnosis was the bane of my life. Both conditions were highly infectious and no treatment made any difference to the outcome which was, inevitably, death. It was much worse for many farmers who were effectively put out of business by the loss of many thousands of piglets. We knew both diseases were viral in origin but could do very little to reduce the losses in a pig herd. Thirty years on there are very few reports of any outbreaks which will come as a great relief to pig farmers with long memories.

We are used as vets to dealing with all sorts of people all the time and indeed it is a part of the job I really do enjoy, but there is a limit: the woman who brought the same dog in three times with chocolate poisoning one Christmas for example! And talking of limits I am immediately reminded of the young mother with a toddler and two flea infested dogs. She declined treatment for her animals as she did not believe they had fleas. She said she could always tell when the dogs had fleas as they (the fleas, not the dog) would jump onto the baby and "you can see them on the baby's bald head." It beats grooming the animal on wet paper I suppose to catch the flea dirt, but it was not a diagnostic technique I had come across before.

It's now many years since I last diagnosed Toxoplasmosis. Then the disease was demonstrated within a colony of semi-feral cats. They had displayed a bewildering variety of symptoms and when I said I diagnosed the disease I would be lying. The laboratory to which I sent both blood and faecal samples came up with the diagnosis of Toxoplasma Gondi, but not the treatment. This is a disease caused by protozoa, organisms about half way in size between a bacterium and a parasitic worm, and it can infect people just as readily as it can cats.

The details of that case are lost in the mists of what is left of my mind, but something stirred in me recently when I

Vet for Hire

was presented with a kitten about four months old which had been rehomed by the Cat's Protection League. Initially it had flu symptoms; runny eyes, sneezing and a small ulcer on its tongue. It responded well to treatment and was vaccinated two weeks later. One week on from the vaccination it came in late on a Monday evening with a head tilt to the left. It was bright and eating, the pupils were equally responsive and there was nothing in either ear to explain why he was perpetually looking around a left hand corner. The owner thought the other cat in the house had biffed him on the ear as Mannie (the kitten) was after all a new comer and interloper into the household. I wasn't so sure and after giving him an injection of antibiotic and anti-inflammatory treatment, I arranged to recheck him next day. Even so I was totally unprepared for the owner to be standing on the doorstep when we opened for business. She was holding Mannie in a towel and he was totally collapsed. He could not stand and the head tilt was even more pronounced. In addition his eyes were twitching and rolling and of an unequal size. His temperature was 106°F and he was very dehydrated. I gave the owner a tentative diagnosis of meningitis and set about taking blood samples and putting him on a drip, but with nothing but severe foreboding with regard to his prospects of survival. I thought he was about to die. The in-house haematology showed quite a high white cell count pointing to infection, but the biochemistry of all his internal organs such as liver and kidneys was normal. It was at this point I reminded myself of the saying "(veterinary) medicine is not just an exact science. There are times it is not a science at all" and sometimes it is just a gut feeling and my gut feeling was screaming Toxoplasmosis!

I have never to my knowledge seen a young animal with such severe central nervous symptoms but I immediately thought I must send off blood for Toxoplasma serum levels. I did not know what else to do diagnostically except to consider a spinal tap which in my limited judgement the patient was in no fit state to undergo.

Vet for Hire....Still

Fortunately Mannie, within a few hours of getting on a drip, was much improved. His temperature dropped to normal and he began to show interest in his surroundings, and by the afternoon would even consider having something to eat. He had more antibiotic into his drip line and by the next day was taking enough interest in food to be able to start on oral antibiotics. His eyes were no longer rolling and twitching except when he tried to move around too much. He still couldn't stand and the head tilt was as pronounced as ever.

Two days later Mannie was well enough to go home. A faecal sample that had been dispatched to the lab was negative for Toxoplasma but the blood sample did confirm a very high concentration of the parasite. This meant that although Mannie had been exposed to the infection, probably from his mother, it did not prove that it was the cause of his neurological complaint. I did, however, feel justified in my warnings to the owner of a possible human health hazard. Toxoplasma can infect people and is especially dangerous for a pregnant woman.

As I write this Mannie is doing well. He is off all medication. He still has the head tilt which I suspect will be permanent, but his owner is happy that he is a healthy, mischievous kitten who is putting on weight and justifying the cost of his diagnostic tests and treatment.

I will miss following all the Mannies in my new part-time locum role as I will inevitably have to pass on many of the more interesting cases to colleagues. Becoming a part-time locum means I will see fewer clients and I will miss following up many interesting cases, even those that at the time caused me to wonder whether it was me going mad or the owners. Even heart breaking cases where the animal has to be put to sleep when nothing else can be done and it is suffering, have all added to my store of veterinary knowledge and experience. I have to admit that I am not too keen on the description 'locum'

Vet for Hire

as it seems to me not to explainfully my new role working as I now do for three different practices. One vicar's wife asked me who I was as she had not met me before. I explained using the locum word and she said that when her husband had retired from his regular parish work but still helped out when required he was not a locum but rather a 'supernumerary.' I have adopted the word. It suits me and seems more fitting somehow.

Full time veterinary practice is for many vets and vet nurses a way of life and can, if you let it, become destructive of family and personal life if there is no room for rest and relaxation.

As with any job there are highs and lows. Some days it can seem, despite your very best endeavours, that even patients who should be responding to treatment do not. Equally, and thankfully, there are just as many occasions when even seemingly hopeless patients get better. This can be difficult for the younger members of the profession who can sometimes despair, especially when they may be feeling isolated in a small practice with no one to talk to and understand. After all their years of study and endeavour they can sometimes feel undervalued, unappreciated and frankly useless. Many good young people are lost to general practice because of this and it is a great pity.

But for me veterinary practice has been a bit like making love in a hammock. To be successful it needs concentration and cooperation from all concerned, but can ultimately be very rewarding and wonderful at times, and a lot of fun.

The End

The Good Life Press Ltd.
The Old Pigsties, Clifton Fields
Lytham Road, Preston
PR4 0XG

The Good Life Press Ltd. is a family run business specialising in publishing a wide range of titles for the smallholder, 'goodlifer' and farmer. We also publish **Home Farmer,** the monthly magazine for anyone who wants to grab a slice of the good life - whether they live in the country or the city. Other Titles of interest:

A Guide to Traditional Pig Keeping by Carol Harris
A-Z of Companion Planting by Jayne Neville
A-Z of Practical Self-Sufficiency by Carl May
Build It! by Joe Jacobs
Build It!.....With Pallets by Joe Jacobs
Building and Using Your Clay Oven by Mike Rutland
Craft Cider Making by Andrew Lea
Garden Projects for Ruffians by Phil Thane
No Time to Grow by Tim Wootton
Poultry Houses from Scratch by Mike Rutland
Precycle! by Paul Peacock
Raising Chickens by Mike Woolnough
Talking Sheepdogs by Derek Scrimgeour
The Frugal Life by Piper Terrett
The Medicine Garden by Rachel Corby
The Polytunnel Companion by Jayne Neville
The Sausage Book by Paul Peacock
The Secret Life of Cows by Rosamund Young
The Smallholder's Guide to Animal Ailments Ed by Russell Lyon
The Smoking and Curing Book by Paul Peacock
Woodburning by John Butterworth
Worms and Wormeries by Mike Woolnough

www.goodlifepress.co.uk

www.homefarmer.co.uk